...talk of atoms every day. ...own up cities, we run sub-... we dream the future with atoms. Of course, we all know that there are atoms—although, except for a few, we've no direct and immediate evidence for them. We assume there are atoms, and we construct images of their internal structure. Of course there are atoms composed of protons, neutrons, and electrons. We would say 'true' of all of that. But where do we stop? What happens when we come to such obscure entities as tachyons? Are there tachyons? Would we say 'true' to the assertion: "There are tachyons"?

Edward MacKinnon works to clarify and describe what happens when we say something is true. Using language analysis, the conceptual revolutions of science, and contemporary theological questions and approaches, he attempts to shed light on this most crucial area of modern thought.

He dispels the notion that language can be divorced from some kind of 'descriptive metaphysics': in any language we are carrying an implicit assumption of what the world is like. He shows that even the technical expression of physics and mathematics is an extension of ordinary language —ordinary language with its implicit world view.

He insists that language cannot be viewed while it is "idling." It is only as language functions, only as people use it to assert or deny, to question and describe, that one can analyze how people are, in fact, using it, and what people mean by the words they use.

and theology. He holds advanced degrees in physics (M.A., Ph.D.), philosophy (M.A., two years as a postdoctoral fellow), and theology (S.T.L.), has written technical articles in each field and many articles on their interrelation.

TRUTH AND EXPRESSION

Truth
and
Expression

The 1968 Hecker Lectures

by

Edward M. MacKinnon

NEWMAN PRESS
New York / Paramus / Toronto

Published by Newman Press
Editorial Office: 304 W. 58th St., N. Y., N. Y. 10019
Business Office: 400 Sette Drive, Paramus, N. J. 07652

Printed and bound in the
United States of America

CONTENTS

To

my parents
who were the first
to teach me what truth is

PREFACE

The invitation to deliver the newly instituted Hecker Lectures at the Wayne State University Newman Center afforded a welcome opportunity to tie together some problem areas which have long intrigued me. How can an analytic approach to the problem of truth be related to new insights into conceptual revolutions and to the hermeneutical principles involved in interpreting a culture different from our own? How can the principles developed be extended to problematic areas of current concern in science and theology? Though the lectures actually delivered did not settle such problems, they did come to grips with them and provided an occasion for a stimulating discussion by an interested and well-informed audience.

These lectures were delivered in May, 1968. Their publication is some three years later. Some explanation of this delay beyond the standard and genuine appeal to too many conflicting commitments seems to be in order. The questions and discussions following each lecture made it clear that more work had to be done on the problems considered. But it was only gradually, as I attempted to rewrite the lectures, that I realized how much more. The first two chapters of the present book are substantially the first two lectures as delivered. They present an analytic approach to the problem of truth which builds on, and hopefully extends, ideas developed by the later Wittgenstein, Sellars, Strawson, and Lonergan. The appendix to

1

Chapter II on "Truth in Aquinas and Heidegger" represents a
belated attempt to answer some searching objections brought
against my original treatment.

Chapters III and IV have each been expanded to about
three times their original size, though for somewhat different
reasons. The original lecture on truth in science could not presuppose an extensive background either in science or in contemporary developments in the philosophy of science. For this
reason the lecture was confined to a fairly general level and
ducked some controverted and really problematic issues. Though
this might have been justifiable, and perhaps even necessary,
in the lecture itself, there seemed to be no good reason to retain
such limitations in the final version. Accordingly, though I retained the format, the style, and even some of the informality
of the lecture actually given, I have expanded it to include a
more detailed explanation of the background epistemological
problems and have extended it to treat some currently controverted issues in the philosophy of science.

The attempt to treat the problem of truth in theology presented a rather different problem centering around limitations
on the part of the speaker, rather than on the part of the audience. As I worked out the lecture and its aftermath, I gradually
came to the realization that my understanding of theology was
severely limited. This lack was not completely explicable in
terms of limitations in my own ability and training. Though I
spent four years studying theology just ten years ago and have
retained an active interest in the field, I am by training a pre-
Vatican II theologian. This Council unleashed forces long
suppressed and initiated a process of reform and renewal whose
further extension seems inevitable and irreversible. I now sub-
scribe to the view that Christianity in general, and Catholicism
in particular, is experiencing a transition of unprecedented
scope, one that will eventually yield a more radical restructur-
ing of Christian life and thought than any renewal since the
Church emerged from persecuted obscurity into an initially
hostile Graeco-Roman world. This radical renewal, in turn, is

inducing a fundamental rethinking of what theology is and how it is to be practiced.

Reactions to such a crisis-situation vary. Many find it threatening. I find it stimulating. Personal reactions aside, I believe that neither the Church nor the cause of truth is well served by any evasion of the truly fundamental problems confronting the present generation. Here, I attempt to face a few of them. But I do so from a specialized point of view, one that could easily be misunderstood. My concern is not to determine which theological propositions are true, but what is entailed by accepting — *aim* any theological proposition as true. This is not agnosticism, nor is it confessional apologetics. It is philosophical analysis attempting to adhere to the methodological presuppositions which structure such a specialized approach. The analysis is hopefully intended to come to grips with contemporary problems. Hence, the urgent need I experienced before, during, and after the lectures to assimilate contemporary developments in theology and to appraise an on-going tradition by examining its historical roots and epistemological presuppositions.

Such an appraisal was not just a question of reading and research, though this was obviously required. It was also a question of dialogue and interaction with those more competent than I in the controverted areas. The first draft of the lecture on truth in theology was presented as a discussion paper for the Boston interdisciplinary theology seminar. I wish to thank the members of this seminar for their comments and to acknowledge some helpful guidance which I have received through discussions with my Jesuit friends, Oliva Blanchette, George MacRae, and Gerald O'Collins. After the Hecker Lectures were given, a redeveloped version of some of these ideas was presented as an address to the *American Catholic Philosophical Association*. Privately circulated copies of this paper were read and commented upon by some theologians whom I wish to acknowledge: Piet Smulders, John Nota, Albert Zabala, and Mary Daly. In this regard I wish especially to thank Rev. N. Max Wildiers, whose friendship, professional competence, and critical judgment contributed greatly to my own rethinking of theology during the eight months we spent together in San Francisco.

In other areas, such extended discussions with competent critical people usually lead to a tempering of radical views. In the present instance the effect was the reverse. My views at the time I was asked to deliver the Hecker Lectures could hardly be considered radical theology. This was not because I found conservative arguments cogent, but because of the inevitable inertia that induces one to coast on positions already assimilated until compelled to admit that continued adherence to such views represents an evasion rather than a solution of pressing problems. In my case, this critical rethinking of accepted views began with the original lecture and has grown in the present account. The inadequacies of this treatment cannot be attributed to the theologians cited. But without their help, the development would have been even less adequate than it is at present.

Finally, I wish to acknowledge some practical assistance received from various sources. I wish to thank the Wayne State University Newman Center for the original invitation. I wish especially to thank the man behind the lectures, Rev. John Kirvan, C.S.P., who issued the original invitation, served as host, and who, in his new post as editor, has patiently borne with my many delays. I wish to thank various communities: the Paulists in Detroit for their generous hospitality; the University of San Francisco, where I stayed as a guest while writing much of this book; my own little community (or commune) and the Jesuits who bore with and even supported my rather idiosyncratic work habits. For typing and other forms of practical assistance I thank Peggy Bender, Mrs. Sophie Yore, Mrs. Marie Allen, and Mrs. Sandra Rasmussen.

I

TRUTH AS
PROBLEMATIC

The general topic to be considered in this series of lectures is the problem of truth. We will begin with the problematic of truth. Subsequent lectures will consider: truth in thought and language; truth in natural science; and truth in theology. The remainder of this introductory lecture should afford a better idea of the type of problems to be considered and the way they will be treated.

Father Kirvan, genial and gracious host of these lectures, originally suggested titling this series: "What Is Truth: A Pilot Project?" To many it might seem more appropriate to title such a series: "What Is Truth: A Parlor Project?" For this question has long functioned as a basic constituent of an indoor sport popular with philosophers, especially in England: parlor epistemology. The participants are expected to lounge in easy chairs or around a seminar table and leisurely discuss abstract questions whose answers have very little practical significance.

Here the concrete, and vitally important, question is: Which statements should be accepted as true? The abstract question is: What does it mean to say that a statement, or a proposition, or whatever it is that 'true' should be predicated of, is true? It might seem that the second question, the abstract one, is of concern primarily, perhaps exclusively, to philosophers who have a vested interest in confusing otherwise clear issues. Without knowing anyone's theory of truth, without even formulating a theory of my own, I can be certain that many statements are, in fact, true. It is true that we are now in Detroit, that today is Friday, that the common sense propositions on which G. E. Moore wished to base philosophy are more certain than any theories that would call their certainty into question. If a child asks the man in the candy store, "What can I buy for a dime?" he would not appreciate an answer concerned with the economic theory of purchasing power. If people are vitally concerned with knowing what is true, do we really help them by trying to clarify what it means to say that a proposition is true?

I believe that we do. If I did not, there would not be much point in my being here. In some important non-philosophical areas of contemporary thought, the abstract philosophical question, "What does it mean to say that something is true?" has become a rather crucial issue. Here, I believe, philosophy finds its real testing ground. If philosophy is to be something more than an academic parlor game, it should be able to contribute to the clarification of truly problematic questions of general concern. Accordingly, I'd like to spend the first half of this lecture considering the significance that the abstract question of truth has in two rather diverse disciplines, the interpretation of science and the development of theology. The selection may seem strange and arbitrary. But, as will be indicated, in both areas the abstract question has become a vital contemporary issue. In the remaining half of this lecture we will consider briefly some established theories of truth and try to determine whether or not they are adequate to the problems considered.

I

TRUTH AND THE INTERPRETATION OF SCIENTIFIC THEORIES

Aristotle, the first and one of the greatest philosophers of *aristotle*

science, hinged his interpretation of scientific systems on a decision as to what types of propositions are to be accepted as true and what it means to say that they are true. Since his interpretation dominated fifteen centuries of thought and conditioned the revolution that eventually replaced his views, it is the logical point of departure in our considerations. When the young Aristotle joined Plato's Academy he was exposed to one of the greatest and least known mathematicians of all time, Eudoxos. Eudoxos' great contribution was the axiomatic method, transforming nascent ideas of scientific explanation from a collection of special recipes for handling different problems into an ordered body of knowledge in which conclusions are derived from principles by logical steps. In this way he was the first to make geometry and astronomy into scientific systems based on principles or hypotheses rather than haphazard collections of statements believed to be true.

Aristotle accepted this deductive ideal of scientific explanation but tried to probe more deeply into its significance by a philosophical examination of the structure, content, and interpretation of scientific systems. The key issue in his opinion was the strength and status of basic principles. In his own words: "Assuming then that my thesis as to the nature of scientific knowledge is correct, the premises of demonstrated knowledge must be true, primary, immediate, better known than and prior to the conclusion, which is further related to them as effect to cause."[1]

If the premises are true and the logic leading from premises to conclusions is correct, then the conclusions must be true. Hence the pivotal importance of the truth of the premises. Here truth is necessary but not sufficient. A statement may be true but trivial. Science should afford not just true conclusions but an explanation of the phenomenon treated. In attempting to understand the views of Aristotle and later Aristotelians on the nature of explanation, it is important to remember that they did not have our present distinction between science and philosophy. The scientist, or natural philosopher, proceeds, Aristotle explains, by the method of analysis and synthesis. Analysis begins with the confused knowledge of ordinary experience and attempts to understand the properties, activities, and natures of bodies by causal analysis. If this analysis succeeds and the true causes become known, then the philosopher can pivot intellectually and begin a synthetic or deductive explanation by using the conclusions of his causal analysis as premises.

In this case, the premises are not only true and certain; they are primary because they are causal. A special sort of correspondence is presupposed here. Beings are determined in what they are and how they act by causal principles: the constitutive causal principles of matter and form; the external causal principles of efficient agents and final causes. If what is first in the order of explanation, the premises, corresponds to what is first in the order of reality, the determining principles of being, then the explanation is truly scientific. The conclusions drawn from the premises are not only true, something guaranteed by the truth of the premises and the correctness of the reasoning; they are also explanatory because they show how beings behave in the light of what these beings really are.

To keep the different views we will be considering in some sort of unified perspective, we can use a simple model. Think of a scientific system as a set of statements running from axioms at the top of the page through theorems, or general conclusions, in the middle of the page, to the particular conclusions at the bottom of the page. Ideally, all the statements are true. But some are true in a primary way, while others are accepted as true because they are correctly inferred from propositions considered true in a primary sense so that the ascription of truth to these propositions is derivative. This primacy in truth is justified by the correspondence between the premises on which scientific explanation is based and the causal and constitutive principles in which the properties and activities of bodies are grounded.

In late Renaissance times, Aristotelianism, the first physical synthesis, crumbled—to be replaced by the new science forged by Copernicus, Kepler, Galileo, Descartes, and especially Isaac Newton. The Newtonianism that emerged represented not merely a new physics, but also a new and rather different idea of what it means to give a scientific explanation. We shall consider these changes only to the degree that they bear on the question of truth in scientific explanation.

Like Aristotle, Newton professed a belief in the method of analysis and synthesis (or composition, to use the Newtonian term). But he interpreted both aspects in a rather novel fashion. Analysis, for Newton, begins with experiments and controlled scientific observation and proceeds by induction to general conclusions. These general conclusions, when sufficiently tested to be accepted as true, served as mathematical premises from which further conclusions could be deduced.[2] As many critics have pointed out, and as Newton himself realized to some extent, this inductive methodology did not really justify the three laws of motion and the law of gravity on which Newton's supreme achievement, his *Principia Mathematica*, was based. These were actually interpreted as laws of nature in a special sense. They were laws built into the very fabric of the universe. Newton did not create them; he discovered them much as Columbus discovered America, because America was already out there waiting to be discovered. The justification for this sort of claim was partially inductive and partially cosmological. In the mechanistic world-view which was emerging, the universe was pictured as a vast clock-work mechanism, a collection of material particles whose motions and interactions were governed by the laws of force. Men believed that there must be such laws. Newton discovered and expressed them.

There are many points of comparison between Newton's views of science and Aristotle's. For our present purpose we will single out one basic difference and one fundamental similarity. The basic difference was the role of causality in explanation. Galileo, Kepler, and Newton all began by accepting the idea that science is an explanation through causes. Yet each in his own way eventually made more progress by disregarding this precept than by following it. Galileo's early studies on motion began with the late medieval concept of *impetus,* a causal concept. Aristotle had explained violent motion by the idea that the mover, e.g., the man throwing a spear, transfers a force to the medium and this force is the causal explanation of the continued motion of the projectile. The *impetus* theory of Bradwardine, Buridan, and Oresme held that the mover transferred a causal force *(impetus)* to the body moved rather than to the medium. Galileo transformed the causal idea of *impetus* into the mathematical idea of inertia and developed the first successful mathematical treatment of projectile motion.

Kepler, more of a Pythagorian, sought the mathematical forms implicit in Tycho Brahe's data on the orbit of Mars. Though he eventually found these—what we now refer to as Kepler's three laws of planetary motion—he felt that this mathematical generalization was not enough to constitute a scientific explanation unless he could give a causal account of the motion. His many attempts to do this in terms of magnetic forces and even through concepts derived from mystical theology ended in failure. Kepler was so discouraged by his own failure to achieve a truly scientific (i.e., causal) explanation that he eventually described his own work as "a pile of dung."

Though Newton often used causal language, he did not base scientific explanation on causal principles in Aristotle's sense of the term 'cause.' He was quite explicit on this point in discussing his law of gravity.[3] In accord with the Aristotelian ideal, which he had been taught, he searched diligently for a physical cause of gravitational attraction, first in terms of ether particles and then in terms of active and passive powers of bodies. Eventually he was able to refute each hypothesis he introduced. But, though he failed to find the cause of gravity, or even a plausible hypothesis concerning such a cause, he did find a general mathematical law describing all gravitational attraction. This, he eventually decided, is what is really basic to scientific explanation: not causal hypotheses, but mathematical laws of general validity.[4]

The point of similarity was in the "top of the page" interpretation of scientific explanation. With Aristotle, Newton
could hold that a scientific system was explanatory only if its
axioms were true, primary, and certain. He would disagree with
the Aristotelian idea that they must be causal principles and
also with the Aristotelian idea that they must be of the same
nature as the conclusions. The very title of Newton's work,
Mathematical Principles of Natural Philosophy, would represent a self-contradiction in an Aristotelian framework. Here,
however, we wish to concentrate on the shared similarities
rather than the differences. Newtonians, like Aristotelians,
could explain the truth and explanatory primacy of their premises by a correspondence view. Newton's laws were thought of
as transcriptions into mathematical language of principles already operative and basic in reality. They could serve as principles of scientific explanations because they already served as
principles of nature.

Newtonianism became, in Kuhn's terms, a new paradigm
for the scientific enterprise. It was not just that Newton's
Principia and *Opticks* were accepted as basic works. His way of
doing science, of attempting to derive mathematical laws from
experiments by induction and interpreting the resultant laws
as principles of nature, ran competition with the Cartesian and
Leibnizian views of scientific explanation as logical deduction
from principles known by intellectual intuition. By the middle
of the eighteenth century Newtonianism had clearly emerged
triumphant. It not only served as the basis of scientific explanation; it set the standards for what it meant to give a scientific
explanation. Subsequent physicists, Euler, Lagrange, Laplace,
d'Alembert and others, could not continue the construction of
the Newtonian edifice without accepting the physical and
logical foundations on which it was built.

Philosophers tended to be more critical. Kant, in particular,
realized that induction could not justify the necessity and universality attributed to fundamental scientific premises. Yet his
stress on the role of synthetic *a priori* principles tended to re-

enforce the "top of the page" interpretation proper to Newtonianism. The truth of a scientific system hinged on the truth of
a special class of propositions, the axioms (or synthetic *a priori*
principles) from which conclusions follow by logical deduction.
These premises must be both true and primary, a requirement
that could be met, it was believed, only if the premises corre-
sponded to principles of nature, or, for Kant, were grounded
in the nature of human cognition.

In the nineteenth century the Newtonian synthesis still
stood as a physical system in spite of the difficulties involved in
trying to reduce the new sciences of thermodynamics and electromagnetic theory to mechanics. However, the critical probing
of men like Whewell and Mill in England and J. B. Stallo and
C. S. Pierce in America made it difficult to accept a simple correspondence interpretation. With Mach, Poincaré and Duhem
at the turn of the century, the special status accorded basic
axioms became a truly critical issue. Mach viewed them as
subjective rules by which the trained observer guides his ex-
pectations. Poincaré interpreted them as conventions, i.e., disguised definitions for the use of such terms as 'mass' and
'acceleration.' For Duhem these axioms were hypotheses to be
appraised, not in terms of their truth, but in terms of their
adequacy in yielding verifiable conclusions.[5] All three effectively rejected the idea, basic to both the Aristotelian and
Newtonian interpretations of science, that the fundamental
laws of science must be expressions of an intelligibility somehow
intrinsic to reality, that the principles of true explanation must
correspond to principles of being.

These criticisms were re-enforced by the then current redevelopments of mathematics: of arithmetic in the hands of
Peano and Frege, and of geometry in the hands of Riemann,
Lobachewsky, Bolyai, and Hilbert. Here the axioms that had
long been thought of as truths somehow intrinsic to the very
fabric of reality were reinterpreted as postulates relative to a
particular and somewhat arbitrary formulation of a specialized
subject matter.

Yet physicists, for the most part, could ignore these criticisms. Their laws, they felt, were verified; their methodology worked; their world-view made reality intelligible. The structure stood secure, regardless of the interpretations critics might draw out of or read into the foundations of that structure. With the twentieth-century revolution wrought by relativity and quantum physics, the structure of this second great physical synthesis crumbled and the transient explanatory union of the conceptual elements we have been considering was dissolved.

Interpreters of the twentieth-century scientific revolution have concentrated, for the most part, on the repudiation of Newtonian determinism, of the mechanistic universe with its ether grounding an absolute space and time, and on a clarification of the new ideas introduced. What was not so clearly recognized, at least at first, was the cumulative effect of the revolutions in physics and mathematics on the problem of truth in the interpretation of scientific systems. The new interpretations that eventually emerged came, not from physics or traditional philosophy, but from research into logic and the foundations of mathematics.

Reflections on the foundations of mathematics led to three positions of philosophical interest: logicism, formalism, and intuitionism.[6] The first of these had the most immediate philosophical impact and is most pertinent to our present problem. Logicism takes its name from the logistic thesis introduced by Frege in 1884 and independently by Bertrand Russell in 1902. The essence of the thesis is the contention that all of mathematics can be derived from logic alone. The monumental *Principia Mathematica* which Whitehead and Russell published between 1910 and 1913 elaborated this thesis into a unified development of logic and mathematics. Though, for technical reasons, the thesis is now generally rejected, at least in the form in which it was originally proposed, the ideal it set forth of a formal unification of scientific knowledge by a logical reduction to basic elements set the pattern for future philosophical thinking.

The first philosophical implementation of this program, Russell's logical atomism, was far from successful. The more profound and more consistent development of logical atomism contained in Wittgenstein's *Tractatus Logico-Philosophicus* proved to be much more influential. What we shall consider here is the use made of Wittgenstein's ideas by the logical positivists, for it was through the highly influential writings of the members of the Vienna Circle that the problem of the truth and interpretation of scientific statements became a vital issue in contemporary thought.

The early logical positivists were quite explicit on their purposes and methods.[7] They wished to establish a firm foundation for the sciences and to demonstrate the meaninglessness of metaphysical and theological statements. The method of accomplishing these aims was the logical analysis of sentence types. From the *Tractatus* they adopted the distinction of all meaningful sentences into analytic and synthetic, or empirical. Analytic statements are either tautologies or contradictions. Though they give no empirical information, their truth value can be determined by an analysis of their logical form. Empirical propositions are either reports of sense experiences (protocol sentences) or finite generalizations from such reports, generalizations whose truth value can be determined only by experimental verification. Metaphysical and theological statements fit into neither category and are dismissed as meaningless pseudo-statements.

This simple division afforded a facile explanation of the truth of scientific statements. Mathematical statements are ultimately tautologies. Though true, they contain no more empirical information than Gertrude Stein's "A rose is a rose is a rose. . . ." Statements in the empirical sciences, such as general laws, are true only to the extent they are verified or—a later modification—admit of the logical possibility of verification. If they do not admit of this possibility, they cannot even be considered candidates for the status of 'true.'

Here we have a complete reversal of the earlier "top of the

page" interpretations of empirical sciences. Like their philosophical predecessors, the positivists hinged the relation be- ←
tween science and reality on the truth of a privileged class of
statements within scientific systems and interpreted 'true' in
terms of a correspondence between what a sentence says and
what is the case. But a combination of an empiricist theory of
knowledge and a rejection of metaphysics in any form necessitated finding this connection only at the "bottom of the page."
The truth and acceptability of a scientific theory depend on the
correspondence between observation reports and particular
conclusions deduced from a statement of general laws and particular boundary conditions.

The trials and tribulations that plagued, modified, and
eventually truncated the short-lived career of the verification —
theory of meaning are probably familiar and need not be re-
counted here.[8] What I wish to do now is to give a schematic
outline of some contemporary positions. Since these will be
discussed in more detail in the third lecture, the outline presented here will be very impressionistic, just enough detail to
locate the problem under consideration.

The transition from early logical positivism to contempo- —
rary positions can be most easily summarized in terms of two
factors. The first is the growth in the unit of meaning. In (1)
syllogistic logic, as in dictionary definitions, the individual term
was considered the basic unit of meaning. In sentential logic,
the sentence, or proposition, functioned as a unit. Then the
emphasis gradually shifted from sentences to systems of sen- —
tences when the technical logical tools were developed to handle
systems as units. The principal tool was the distinction between
object languages and metalanguages. If the system under consideration is logically reconstructed in the form of an object
language, or uninterpreted formal calculus, then one can speak
of interpreting it in terms of two types of metalanguages: a
syntactical metalanguage, concerned with rules for formation
and transformation of sentences; and a semantical metalanguage, concerned with meaning, denotation, and truth. Though

such a purely formal analysis of systems of thought has its own limitations, its elaboration did serve a liberating function.

The second change-inducing factor is the fusion of elements drawn from logical positivism, linguistic analysis, and pragmatism. To see the significance of this fusion, think of knowledge, or at least a logical reconstruction of what can be stated as knowledge, as a collection of systems. The first system, and the one which forms a methodological base for any other system, is ordinary language. Though it is not a theory, it is possible to extract a theory from it by making explicit the basic view of the world implicit in ordinary language and labeling it 'descriptive metaphysics,' a subject that will be discussed in more detail in the next lecture. The other systems would not all be sciences. However, to clarify and simplify the structure of the argument we will assume that the other systems to be considered are branches of science rationally reconstructed in accord with the norms set by logicians.

Each system has its own ontic commitments, that is, a commitment to the things one speaks about in using the system. Thus, if one is speaking the language of molecular physics, the existence of molecules is presupposed. For the benefit of the logicians in the audience we may put this idea of ontic commitments in slightly more technical language. The fundamental axioms of the system must include existentially quantified statements using basic category terms. Then one using a theory to explain a domain of reality is ontically committed to the existence of the entities whose names serve as the values of the variables in these existentially quantified statements. This is often summarized in Quine's dictum: to be is to be the value of a variable.[9]

Classical philosophers spoke of the great chain of being. Our contemporary analogue is the great hierarchy of systems. With this as a background we may return to the problem of the interpretation of formal systems. It is possible to hold this system-centered view and still cling to a "bottom of the page" interpretation of scientific systems, as Carnap and, in a way,

Hempel still do. Carnap interprets ontic commitments as statements which are analytic within a given system and therefore not factual claims at all. The key sentences, accordingly, are ultimate conclusions which must be related to observation statements by means of correspondence rules. If one gets away from internal statements made within the system and considers the external question of the system as a whole then, in Carnap's opinion, one is concerned with the pragmatic question of whether or not the system should be accepted rather than with the factual question, "Is it true?" Thus the statement, "There are molecules" spoken within the framework of molecular physics would be accepted as true but trivial. Within this system it is simply a tautology. If one wishes to prescind from molecular physics as a system and insist that there *really* are molecules, this might seem to be a metaphysical or existential claim concerning a certain category of beings. But, Carnap insists, it can be analyzed without significant residue as a practical decision to accept the system of molecular physics as a basis for explanation.[10]

A modification of this view could be dubbed a "middle of the page" interpretation of scientific systems. Campbell, Braithwaite, and, most significantly, Ernest Nagel have defended the view that the basic mode of interpreting scientific systems actually operative in the development of science is by a correspondence between general conclusions derived within a system and inductively established empirical generalizations.[11] Thus, Newtonian mechanics was accepted as explanatory because it yielded Kepler's laws; the kinetic theory because it yielded the gas laws; Bohr's theory of the atom because it reproduced Balmer's laws for spectral lines. These theories, in fact, did more than yield these already established laws; they also corrected them, generalized them, and showed the limits of their applicability. Here, as earlier, scientific systems could be interpreted in terms of three basic components: a theoretical system, an observational system, and correspondence rules linking the two. Now, however, the key correspondence rules are between empirical generalizations and theorems derived from the axioms. This modifies the "bottom of the page" interpretation but still shares with it a key assumption. The physical interpretation of a theoretical system depends on translation into or correspondence with key sentences formulated in the observation language.

Such a method of interpreting scientific systems has recently come under sharp criticism in the writings of Sellars, Feyerabend, Smart and others.[12] What is rejected is not the correspondences discussed above but the explanatory significance attached to these correspondences. The chief objection is to the idea that theoretical statements and systems acquire a physical significance only when they are given this significance by a correspondence with observation language statements. Of the various criticisms offered, I will list the two that seem most pertinent to our present concerns. The first is epistemological and is directed against "the myth of the given," or the naive epistemology implicit in the views of interpretation through correspondence rules. Central to the myth is the idea that the basic category terms used to make observation reports are either given in perception or somehow derived by immediate abstraction from perception, a quasi-automatic process. If this were so, then this observation language would be essentially immune to conceptual revision. This, in fact, is the role it plays in the interpretations just discussed. Since theoretical systems acquire physical significance only by means of translation into observation language, the observation language itself is the basis of all physical meaning and is essentially immune to conceptual revision. However, the type of analysis to be discussed in more detail in the next lecture shows that the category terms of ordinary language cannot be explained in terms of givenness. They are not directly given either by reality, or by perception, or by some automatic process of abstraction.

The second basic difficulty is theoretical or scientific. Explanatory theories involve commitments to such theoretical entities as genes, atoms, and fundamental particles. These entities are not directly given in sense experience. Nor are their names a part of the ordinary language framework. If observation-centered interpretations are ultimately normative, then such entities, mentioned in the theoretical language but not in the observational language, must be accorded the status of theoretical constructs, or useful scientific fictions. They cannot name physically real entities if they are not a part of the language which serves as the basis for determining physical meaning. Yet scientists, as well as an increasing number of philosophers, believe in the real existence of such theoretical entities and are notably unwilling to accept correspondence rules as a new universal solvent capable of dissolving the real existence of atoms and particles.

The alternative to these observation-centered interpretations of scientific systems is to take theories seriously. Think again of the hierarchy of systems. The significant question—and it is really a pragmatic question—is: Which theories are to be accepted as basic in giving explanations and in describing material reality? If there are good reasons for accepting a theory as explanatory, there are equally good reasons for accepting the entities postulated or presupposed by the theory as real. In addition to what was said earlier concerning ontic commitments of theories or conceptual frameworks, there is one further norm operative here: reducibility. A simple example may clarify this. Classical thermodynamics implicitly accepts a gas as a special type of substance with temperature, pressure, and volume as distinctive properties. The classical gas laws of Boyle, Charles, Gay-Lussac, etc., had this idea as their conceptual underpinning. Kinetic theory conceives of a gas as a collection of molecules in motion. According to a "middle of the page" interpretation, the validity of kinetic theory is established, at least partially, by the fact that within the framework of kinetic theory one can derive, correct, and extend the classical gas laws provided one accepts the basic correspondence rule relating the temperature of a gas to the average kinetic energy of the molecules. But the ontic commitments of the two theories are different. Accepting kinetic theory as explanatory entails accepting the reality of the entities posited by kinetic theory, molecules in motion. More generally, the question of real ontic commitments is determined by the question of which theories and theoretical frameworks are accepted as explanatory and irreducible. Ordinary language has a privileged status in issues concerning the ground of meaning and the basis of language extension. But it does not have this status when the point at issue is one of describing and explaining reality.

And so philosophers, some at least, have returned to a "top of the page" interpretation of scientific systems. The basic interpretative link between scientific systems and whatever it is they explain comes once again from the privileged status accorded basic axioms. In the new interpretations, however, these axioms do not correspond with causal principles or laws of nature. The correspondence presupposed is a minimal one, a function commitment to the reality of the entities whose names serve as the values of variables in irreducible explanatory theories.

From this historical overview one fundamental question emerges. Need the interpretation of scientific systems hinge on the truth and primacy accorded a special sub-group of scientific sentences, whether axioms, laws, or conclusions? Since I am lecturing in Detroit, an adaptation of the Ford slogan might not be out of place. There must be a better idea. We will return to this problem in the third lecture.

II

TRUTH AND EXPRESSION IN THEOLOGY

The problem of truth in theology can be discussed much more succinctly since the problematic is more straightforward. Contemporary philosophers often question the meaningfulness of religious statements. Yet, in a basic sense, there is no real doubt about their meaningfulness. Thus, Christians, the group we will focus on, have little difficulty in understanding each other. The real question is: Is it reasonable to accept theological statements as true? One could attempt to answer such a question in various rather different ways. I will concentrate on one approach in the hope that it might be of some service to theologians as well as philosophers.

Believers in a religious tradition do have a commitment to truth. Theology, for Christians, is grounded in the *a priori* acceptance of the truth of whatever God has revealed. Revelation is not identical with a set of statements. However, any attempt to clarify and explain what has been revealed necessarily entails a critical examination of the sources through which this revelation has been communicated to us. The practice of the Christian Churches, Catholic, Protestant, and Orthodox, manifests a belief in the possibility of extracting from this tradition propositions which should be accepted as true: the creeds of the early Church, the declarations of the Ecumenical Councils, the confessional statements of different denominations. Without this possibility of the affirmation of statements or doctrines as true, any idea of revealed truth would indeed be nebulous.

Our concern here will be primarily with the question of what is entailed in accepting any such statements as true, rather than with the question of which statements are in fact true. Though the subject matter is theological, the approach will be analytical rather than confessional. This rather abstract question: "What is entailed in accepting a theological statement or a collection of such statements as true?" has assumed a critical significance in two areas of current theological interest.

The first area could be labeled 'metascriptural studies' since this rather arbitrary tag draws attention to the epistemological problems concerned with scriptural interpretations in a way that the more general and more familiar term 'biblical theology' does not. For those Christians somewhat loosely labeled orthodox, an acceptance of Christianity entails an acceptance of the truth of whatever the Sacred Scriptures teach or affirm. But what does Scripture teach or affirm? For an extreme fundamentalist the answer is simple and straightforward. Each sentence of Scripture is true as it stands. But most Scripture scholars, conscious of the vast differences between the conceptual systems, or world-views, of the authors of Scripture and our own view, and increasingly aware of the different literary forms and ecclesiastical concerns that shaped the texts we now have, do not want to link the truth of revelation to the truth of individual sentences. This raises a basic epistemological problem. What does it mean to speak of the truths attested by Scripture if one refrains from affixing the predicate 'true' to individual sentences?

A clarification of what the Scriptures do teach is the proper concern of those professionally competent in this area—and I am not a member of this in-group. But their work has engendered epistemological problems concerning the relation between the truth affirmed and the sentences, whether of Scripture or of the exegete's summary of what he takes to be the teaching of Scripture, which serve as the vehicle for the affirmation of this truth. Here, it is hoped, a more adequate explanation of what it means to say that something is true would be of distinct service.

The second problematic area concerns the development of doctrine. In the past both Catholics and Protestants have resisted the idea that there can be any real development of doctrine beyond a subjective growth in understanding a content that remains essentially unchanged and unchangeable. Protestants, at least conservative Protestants, did this because they felt that their faith was founded on Scripture rather than on an on-going ecclesiastical tradition. Catholics did this because they held that revelation ended with the death of the last apostle and that further doctrinal development was only a question of making explicit what was already implicit in this revelation.

Doctrinal development, however, is an historical fact. A study of the history of Christian tradition has compelled most theologians to accept this. According to the late Father John

Courtney Murray, acceptance of real doctrinal development —
was the fundamental issue separating liberals and conservatives
at the recent Vatican Council. Most of the decrees promulgated
represent the convictions of the liberals who accepted the reality
of doctrinal development as a part of the Christian tradition.

Yet any acceptance of doctrinal development as something
more than making explicit what was already implicit raises the
question of the truth value of such past statements as creedal
affirmations and conciliar decrees. Does the acceptance of these
as true imply that alternative, even apparently contradictory
formulations are necessarily false? To answer "Yes" is to deny
any real possibility of objective doctrinal development. To
answer "No" is to raise the question: "What does it really mean
to say that a statement, such as a creedal affirmation, should be
accepted as true?"

III
THEORIES OF TRUTH

The final part of this introductory lecture will survey some
theories on the nature of truth. This may be done briefly, for
we do not intend to give either a detailed exposition or a
critical evaluation. Elements from each of the theories considered will reappear in the next lecture—though transformed
into shapes the original authors might not recognize. What
follows, accordingly, is a superficial exposition coupled to a
preliminary evaluation.

First there are the three rather well-known classical positions: the correspondence, coherence, and pragmatic theories
of truth.[13] The correspondence theory takes its origin from the
common sense view that the sentence, "This paper is white," is
true if, and only if, this paper is indeed white. The promotion
of this type of common sense reflection into a full-scale theory
takes a different form in the Aristotelian-Scholastic, the Empiricist, and the Marxist traditions, though each affirms a corre-

spondence theory of truth. The Scholastic tradition, in particular, centers on the definition of truth as a conformity between the mind and reality.

The difficulties involved in promoting the correspondence view into a full-scale theory of truth are rather well known. The theory is at its best when dealing with empirical statements, though even here there is a penumbral vagueness in explaining what it means to say that the mind conforms to reality. Difficulties multiply when one attempts to use a correspondence definition of truth as the basis for explaining other types of sentences which are, in fact, accepted as true: analytic statements, tautologies, conditionals—especially contrary to fact conditionals, futurables, etc. A difficulty of a different sort comes from the abiding temptation to use this *theory* of truth as a *norm* for deciding which statements are to be accepted as true. Yielding to this temptation generally presages a fall into the conceptual bog known as naive realism. Such difficulties notwithstanding, I believe that the correspondence theory has a core of correctness, a core which we will attempt to extricate and elaborate in subsequent lectures.

The coherence theory explains truth as a relation of judgments, not to reality, but to other judgments. A judgment, embodied in a statement, should be accepted as true only if it is coherent with other judgments already accepted as true. There is, I believe, a valuable insight here. But it is an insight into the importance of systems in knowledge and of coherence in systems, not an insight into the meaning of 'true.' We have little difficulty in accepting as true judgments which are not coherent with previous judgments whenever we feel that the facts dictate such a judgment. A more basic difficulty is that the coherence theory, upon analysis, seems to depend upon the type of correspondence view it ostensibly rejects. What does it mean to say that two judgments are coherent? Logicians have examined this question, or at least a special instance of it, in great detail: What does it mean to say that a set of statements, e.g., axioms, are consistent? The answer is that the set is consistent only if there is at least one interpretation in which every sentence of the set is true. In other words, a clarification of the meaning of 'consistent' or 'coherent' presupposes that one already knows what it means to say that a sentence is true. This, in turn, implies that one cannot explain 'true' in terms of coherence without some degree of circularity in the defining process.

'The pragmatic theory of truth' is a blanket term used to (3) cover the rather different views of Pierce, James, and Dewey. The critics of this view—and anyone writing on it today is almost invariably a critic rather than a defender—can easily lift a few phrases from William James' popular lectures and claim that the pragmatic doctrine is that to say an idea is true means that it works. William James, however, was not so much trying to deny the correspondence view of truth as to go beyond it. He thought of truth as a property of beliefs rather than of objects and rather rhetorically inquired into what it really means to say that beliefs accord with objects if we cannot do anything significant about manifesting this accord and making it fruitful.[14] The basic difficulty with his view is not so much its falsity as its obscurity. If we distinguish between a clarification of the meaning of 'true' and the reasons why we accept certain propositions as true, then the pragmatic account of truth is of little help in the question of clarification, but it does supply some valuable insights into the latter question. I point this out because we shall be using some of these ideas later when we discuss the pragmatic theory of acceptance.

One feature these approaches, especially the first two, have in common is that they rely on a *theory* of truth and try to interpret disputed cases by fitting them into a general theoretical framework. A rather different approach, and one which I find appealing, is to begin by clarifying the way the word 'true' already functions in language usage. Though such an analysis does not of itself supply a theory of truth, it does supply the subject matter which any theory of truth must explain. Ideally it supplies such subject matter in a theory-neutral way. This is helpful, for if a theory is used to determine what count as facts and how these facts are to be interpreted, then claims that a theory must be correct because it fits the facts are not very convincing. Accordingly we shall consider briefly two recent attempts to explain, not truth, but the role the word 'true' plays in ordinary language. As John Austin put it: "*In vino, possibly, veritas,* but in a sober symposium, '*verum.*'"[15]

The first of these views stems from the work of A. Tarski on the semantic definition of truth. The significance of his work is often misunderstood, especially when it is referred to as the semantic *theory* of truth and interpreted as a correspondence theory. What Tarski did was to construct a consistent semantical definition of 'true sentence.' This clarification played a vital role in establishing the need for semantical metalanguages to interpret formal languages, a theme that Carnap developed in more detail. But what Tarski did in explaining the role of 'true' in such sentences as: " 'Snow is white' is true if and only if snow is white," was not really a clarification of the way 'true' functions in ordinary language. It was, rather, an attempt to regiment ordinary language by giving a single unambiguous definition of 'true' which would be free from such semantic contradictions as the liar paradox. This clarifies ordinary usage only in a minimal and rather formal sense. That is, it explains the fact that 'true' is a predicate which takes sentences as subjects, provided certain necessary and sufficient conditions are met. But such semantical rules for the proper predication of 'true' are not sufficient either for a full explanation of the meaning of 'true' nor as an explanation of the varied related usages this term has in English.

The final position to be considered, sometimes referred to as the assertive-redundancy (A-R) view, was suggested by Ramsey and developed by Strawson.[16] It does concentrate on the role that 'true' plays in ordinary language. To see the simple idea hiding behind this impressive label, consider the two sentences:

(1) This wall is yellow.

(2) The statement, "This wall is yellow," is true.

What does (2) really add to (1)? Strawson would answer that it adds nothing cognitively significant. It is essentially a special type of performative utterance, or a special way of emphasizing the original utterance. To say that a statement is true is not to make a further statement at all; it is to make the same statement in a more emphatic way.

This interpretation has been criticized on analytic grounds by Austin,[17] Geach,[18] Ezorsky,[19] and others. Since these difficulties will be considered in the next lecture, we will simply consider the question of whether these clarifications of 'true,' which we have treated rather cavalierly, are adequate to the problems already considered. In the survey of interpretations of science, the problem of truth had a peculiar status. In an ideal scientific system, all the propositions contained in it from the first axioms to ultimate conclusions are true. But the truth of some propositions is derivative. They are known to be true because they are correctly deduced from propositions whose truth is known by non-deductive means. The crucial question, accordingly, was: Which propositions are to be considered true in a non-derivative way? The various answers proposed depend, at least in part, on differing theories of truth. What would either the semantic definition of 'true' or the A-R position contribute to this problem?

The answer, I am afraid, is only too clear. They would contribute nothing at all. Both positions apply 'true' uniformly to all the propositions in our ideal system. The semantic definition would lead to such assertions as: "The sentence 'The electron has spin one-half' is true if and only if the electron has spin one-half." The A-R analysis might teach us how to assert such positions more emphatically. Neither would afford any basis for distinguishing among true sentences those which are true in a primary way and those whose truth is derivative. But this is the crucial problem, a problem which grew out of differing views of the nature of truth.

Nor, unfortunately, are these views adequate for the theological problems considered. Both are geared to cover sighted cases rather than blind cases. That is, they apply to explicitly formulated sentences of which 'true' is predicated, whether as a metalinguistic comment or as a rhetorical device. But what of the case where one says that whatever Scripture teaches is true, but does not equate the teaching of Scripture with an explicit affirmation of particular sentences contained in Scripture? This surely is the case with Scripture scholars who accept the authority of Scripture and then undertake an exhaustive examination to determine what it is that Scripture actually teaches. No clarification of 'true' which weds its usage exclusively to the explicit formulation of sentences or statements is adequate to cover this case.

This survey of theories of truth was manifestly inadequate, both in scope and depth. But, I believe, it did serve to specify the initial problem confronting us: What does it mean to say that something is true? A reasonable way to begin, I believe, is with a clarification of the way 'true' functions in ordinary language. Necessary as this is, it is not sufficient unless we wish to confine ourselves to parlor epistemology. Eventually, in the third and fourth lectures, we will have to attempt a more general view of truth that can come to grips with the formidable problems considered earlier. I would like to say "will present" rather than "will attempt," but this would manifest an over-optimism bordering on idiocy. However, we will begin and see how far we can go.

II

THE MEANING
OF 'TRUE'

Science and philosophy exhibit a peculiar anti-parallelism in their methods of development. In science each generation builds on the work of its predecessors. Even scientific revolutions presuppose a background of conceptual continuity and growth. Philosophy may seem to follow a similar pattern if one is focusing on developments within a particular school of thought. But an overall view presents a rather different picture. Science is like a rising tide in which each new wave spends itself in contributing to a general advance. Each new wave in philosophy seems to dissolve the work of its predecessors by calling into question presuppositions and ways of viewing the world and the task of the philosopher that earlier generations assumed as essentially unproblematic.

For the medieval Scholastics philosophy was an objective science. Though they realized, of course, that there could be no knowing without a knower and that the philosopher, accordingly, must consider what knowledge is, subjectivity as such was not a part of philosophy. After Descartes, the role of the subject was no longer unproblematic. Yet, by involving the veracity of God as a guarantee of the essential validity of external knowledge, he did not really question whether our way of knowing determines the nature-for-us of the known. Kant's Copernican revolution undercut this and other presuppositions of his predecessors. Yet his attempt to determine the capacity of the mind to know reality implicitly assumed that language, as an expression of thought, is essentially unproblematic. He could focus on thought and presuppose the meaningfulness of language. The contemporary development of analytic philosophy has undercut this assumption.

This historical process of undercutting, of calling into question positions and presuppositions which earlier generations either accepted as unproblematic or failed to question because there seemed to be no other way of viewing the matter, should supply something of a general orientation in treating such a perennial philosophical problem as the nature of truth. Earlier generations approached this by developing theories of truth, theories leading to precise definitions of truth such as the traditional, *"Veritas est adequatio rei et mentis."* What contemporary accounts call into question are not so much particular definitions or theories but the presuppositions implicit in any attempt to treat this problem by defining 'truth' or explaining its essence.

Heidegger brings out these presuppositions through what he calls 'the paradox of truth.'[1] Anyone developing a theory of truth has a goal which supplies norms for judging the efficacy of his endeavors. The goal is to develop an explanation which gives a true account of the matter treated, i.e., to present a *true* theory of truth. The very attempt to develop such a theory and to judge its success implicitly presupposes that one already knows what 'true' means.

An analyst would get at the same point through the notion of language games and families of meanings. 'Language games' refer to language as used in particular types of contexts. Rather than summarize Wittgenstein, we can apply his type of approach to the problem at hand. In a very real sense, all of us already know the meaning of 'true,' for we know how to use the word in different contexts and can recognize incorrect usages. If we reflect on our normal linguistic practice, we soon realize that 'true,' like so many basic terms, has rather different uses in different contexts. We speak of 'true love' and 'the true dimensions of the problem.' We may say that a defendant's alibi is not true; that a whale is a true mammal; that events proved a prediction true; that it is necessarily true that the sum of the angles in a Euclidean triangle equals two right angles; but it is not necessarily true that the cat is on the mat. Our spontaneous impulse—spontaneous, granted our historical conditioning—is to search for the essence exemplified in these instances, for the common core of meaning proper to these varied examples. But this way of approaching the problem reflects the presupposition that there is such a thing as a common essence exemplified in varied fashions.

Language does not function quite that way. We can speak of a family resemblance shared by the many members of the Kennedy clan. This does not mean a common essence, Kennedyness, but a resemblance in profile in one case, in mannerisms in another, in face structure in another. Just as each Kennedy has a face that is distinctively his own, so each of the varied usages indicated has a meaning that is distinctively its own. The meaning, in fact, is explicated in terms of the way the word is used in different contexts or language games. Yet, to jumble metaphors, it is often possible to pick out one language game in which a particular word has its native habitat. Thus, 'circle' has many varied uses: "The pilot circled the field"; "She belonged to a literary circle"; "The argument was circular," etc. Yet few, I believe, would question the contention that the primary use of 'circle' is the geometric one, that this is the host on which the others are, to varying degrees, parasites.[2]

Similarly, we may ask what is the primary use of 'true' in ordinary language. This does not imply a basic meaning to which other meanings may be reduced. It is, rather, a base which admits of different extensions and analogous usages—but of that later. Some candidates may be eliminated rather easily: the true mammal and the statement that is true because analytic. There are, I believe, only two serious contenders for the role of the primary use of 'true' in ordinary language. These could be called the 'factual' and the 'moral,' where the labels serve more to locate language games than to prescribe meanings. In the factual usage, a statement (or proposition, or whatever it is that 'true' is predicated of) is labeled 'true' if it is in accord with what is believed to be the case in reality. The moral usage, distinguishing between telling the truth and telling a lie, clearly presupposes that one knows what it means to tell the truth, i.e., that one already knows the factual meaning of 'true.'

We shall, accordingly, begin by focusing on the use of 'true' in factual claims. It is here, I believe, that the meaning of the term is first assimilated by the young language learner. The more extended and specialized usages will be considered after we have considered the base of which they are extensions. The questions we shall consider are: What is 'true' properly predicated of? Why and when is it so predicated? What are the larger implications of this usage? The attempt to analyze these technical questions will inevitably make this lecture more formal—or should I say "duller"—than the others. But an analytic clarification is necessary for any consistent advance.

I

'TRUE' AS A PREDICATE

What is 'true' properly predicated of? To sort out the various contenders—sentences, propositions, statements, assertions, beliefs, and states of mind—consider the following sentences:

(1) The pencil is on the table.
(2) Le crayon est sur la table.
(3) The pencil is on the table.

Traditionally it is claimed that what we have here are three utterances (or inscriptions), two sentences, and one proposition. Some would make further distinctions and claim that (1), for example, is a statement rather than a mere sentence only when it is considered as uttered by a particular individual in a definite context. Those stressing assertions as the vehicle of truth-claims would distinguish between simply presenting (1) as a hypothesis and asserting it as true. The difference is dependent upon the intention of the speaker and suggests a consideration of mental acts, such as judgments, or states, such as beliefs.

Our immediate concern is with the distinction between sentences and propositions. A tradition common to Scholasticism, classical empiricism, rationalism, and Marxism attributes 'true' to propositions, with sentences merely serving as a vehicle for propositions. A proposition is the meaning of a sentence. But this tradition has its difficulties. The claim that sentences (1) and (2) express the same proposition entails the consequence that neither of them is the expressed proposition. What then is a proposition as distinct from a sentence? To answer that it is the *meaning* of a sentence seems to reify meanings as a rather peculiar disembodied class of abstract entities. Propositions are like sentences—except that they are not sentences in any particular language. But what is like a sentence that is not a sentence? Dissatisfaction with such abstract entities has led many logicians, especially the Polish school and W. Quine,[3] to concentrate on sentences, i.e., inscriptions on a piece of paper or marks in some other medium, as the basic subject of which 'true' is properly predicated.

This Tarski-Quine position is counter-intuitive and quite nominalistic. We readily accept equivalent sentences as making the same truth claim. Its justification is really a negative one, the rejection of abstract entities. Unless we can clarify the meaning of 'meaning' without making of it a disembodied reality, we cannot give a coherent doctrine of propositions. Here, I believe, Sellars, building on the work of Wittgenstein and others, has supplied the necessary clarification.[4] The meaning of a word is essentially the role it plays in a language game.

When I say "'rot' means red," I am not establishing a relation between a German word and a meaning signified by 'red.' Rather, I am presupposing that you already know how to use the word 'red' and informing you that the word *mentioned,* 'rot,' has the same role in language games played on the other side of the Rhine that the word *used,* 'red,' has in our language games. This does not presuppose abstract entities, but two different yet similar language games and people who know how to play them.

In a similar way, a proposition is clarified by the role a sentence plays in language as used. By 'sentence' we mean a collection of words or sounds bound into a linguistic unit by appropriate syntactical and semantical rules. Unless a sentence is used in such a way as to refer to something extra-linguistic, something beyond itself, the predication of 'true' is inappropriate except in the trivial derivate sense of an analytically true sentence. A proposition is a sentence as used. If other sentences can play essentially the same role, they will be counted as the same proposition. The use to which sentences are put, in making ordinary language factual claims, centers on the problem of reference. In factual claims the subject is the referential term. The predicate is attached to the subject but predicated of the supposit for which the subject stands. 'Snow' is not white; but snow is. 'Referring' I take to be an intentional term. It is something done by persons. 'Denotation' is an extensional term, a linguistic operation clarified by semantical rules. However, people refer by using the means made available through language and conceptualizations of reality embodied in linguistic systems. The category terms available in a particular language specify the sorts of things that one can refer to by means of language. In this sense, which Cornmann has recently clarified,[5] reference must be considered internal to a linguistic system. Working from quite a different perspective, Levi-Strauss has given a fascinating account of the types of category terms that radically different language systems employ.[6] Such cross-cultural comparisons are quite helpful in dissipating the idea that the category terms we use are simply determined by what things are in themselves.

If someone here were a mind-reader or adept at the more esoteric forms of ESP discussed in science-fiction, he would, I suspect, be getting some strong reports from some members of the audience. "Hasn't this speaker ever heard of the theory of definite descriptions and the work of Russell, Quine and a veritable army of logicians?" Linking reference to the use of a subject inevitably involves the ambiguities and paradoxes proper to speech about gold mountains and non-existent French kings. Here, I believe, we have a situation similar to the one noted earlier when discussing Tarski's semantic definition of 'true.' What the logicians are looking for is one rule or clarification which will unambiguously apply to all cases in a univocal way. This is the way the laws of logic work. But it is not the way ordinary language works. The meaningfulness of ordinary language depends on presuppositions which may be roughly classified as: ontological, or the conceptualization of reality implicit in the language used; linguistic, or the rules that structure words into meaningful sentences; and dialectical, or the shared presuppositions of a dialogue. The existence of the referent denoted by the subject term is generally such a dialectical presupposition. I cannot carry on a conversation with any of you about the qualities and capabilities of the different presidential candidates unless we both accept the fact—though we need not state it—that there really are people named Richard Nixon and Hubert Humphrey.

In the same vein it must be admitted that my distinction between sentences and propositions is a bit artificial. In ordinary speech we are concerned only with sentences as used, i.e., with propositions, and not with sentences considered as linguistic entities. Hence, we would ordinarily indicate agreement by saying: "What you said is true," or "Your statement is true," but rarely if ever by saying: "Your proposition is true" (unless 'proposition' is being used in the sense of 'proposal'). This usage does not indicate that 'true' is not properly predicated of propositions. It rather indicates that a distinction between propositions, considered as roles, and sentences, considered as vehicles playing that role, is the concern of those who analyze language rather than of those who simply use it.

'True' is predicated primarily of propositions, or of linguistic units called sentences considered as role players. To get at the question of *why* propositions are labeled 'true,' let us consider a different opinion, one that relates truth to judgments rather than sentences. As Lonergan expressed it:[7]

It follows, then, that properly speaking expression is not true or false. Truth pertains to the judgment inasmuch as it proceeds from a grasp of the virtually unconditioned, inasmuch as it conforms to the being it affirms, and inasmuch as it demands an intrinsic intelligibility in being as a condition of the possibility of knowing. Expressions are instrumental. . . . But in themselves expressions are merely adequate or inadequate. . . . However, this account of the relation between truth and expression rests on the position that truth resides in the internal act of judgment, of assenting and dissenting.

His position, which is generally shared by the transcendental Thomists, seems to contradict the position I have been developing linking 'true' and propositions. To consider Lonergan's position in a bit more detail we should outline the salient features of his theory of knowledge. He distinguishes three levels of knowledge: experience, understanding, and judgment. By 'experience' he means basically perception, though he does not, in my opinion, give an adequate account of the relation between perception and perception reports. The level of understanding is a two-step process. Insight is the grasp of a unity, relation, or wholeness potentially present in the data of experience. It is expressed by means of a concept, definition, or hypothesis. Judgment is also a two-step process. If pre-judgmental reflection grasps evidence sufficient to warrant assent, e.g., to the hypothesis proposed on the level of understanding, then one may affirm the proposition. Judgment, in the strict sense, is the mental act grounding this affirmation or negation. Truth is claimed to reside in the internal act of judgment because it is only here that a truth-claim is made.

Here, I believe, we must make a distinction between making a truth-claim and that of which 'true' is properly predicated. It is only in a judgment, considered as a mental act, or in an assertion, considered as the resulting linguistic performance, that a truth-claim is made. But 'true' is not predicated, except in a derivative sense, of this act of judgment but of the proposition which was considered as a candidate for the status of being true. The function of pre-judgmental reflection is to decide whether or not the hypothesis being considered should be affirmed. To affirm it is to make an implicit claim that it is true. This is something that is brought out in a slightly different way by assertive-redundancy analysis. But asserting a proposition does not change either the meaning or the referential function of the proposition in question. We may summarize this by saying that it is through a judgment of affirmation that one makes a truth claim. One does this either implicitly, by affirming a proposition, or explicitly, by quoting the proposition and predicating 'true' of it.

Before tying this together, we should consider one final candidate: statements. The word 'statement' has various overtones. As Austin explains it, a statement differs from a sentence in that a statement is an historic event, an utterance attributable to a definite individual in a particular context.[8] Thus, one speaks of the English sentence, "This war is unjust," but of *my statement,* "This war is unjust." Austin contends that 'true' is properly predicated (or denied) of the latter, but not of the former, of statements, but not of sentences. Here, I believe, it is necessary to distinguish three different features: the proposition in question, the utterance of it considered as an historical event, and the affirmation implicit in the statement considered as performative. The last point, affirmation, has already been considered. With regard to the other two, we may quote Strawson's reply to Austin: "'My statement' may be either what I said or my saying of it. My saying something is certainly an episode. What I say is not. It is the latter not the former that we declare to be true."[9]

There is, however, one further point that is brought out, though somewhat indirectly, by Austin's claim. We linked 'true' to propositions, where a proposition was interpreted as a sentence playing a role. For ordinary language factual claims, the prime analogate for the predication of 'true,' an essential aspect of this role is the use of referential terms or devices in the actual predication. When considering a sentence such as "Caesar crossed the Rubricon" or "A hydrogen atom has one proton," reference can be clarified without considering the speaker. But this is not so for any sentence containing token-reflexive terms (i.e., personal pronouns, or such terms as 'here,' 'there,' 'this,') or the use of context-dependent definite articles (the cat is on the mat). In such cases the intended meaning of the proposition cannot be clarified without considering the statement as an historic event. But even here the bestowal or denial of 'true' depends on the relation of what is said to that of which it is said rather than to the person saying it.

The viable point that these people have been making in their different ways is that predicating 'true' of a proposition is roughly equivalent to asserting the proposition. That is, the role of 'true' as a metalinguistic predicate proper to propositions is equivalent to the role of judging, in Lonergan's sense, or to asserting as the correlative linguistic performance. This, it should be noted, is not a definition of 'true.' To define a term is to reduce it to terms that are more basic—or at least more familiar—than the term being defined. Any such process must ultimately terminate in terms which admit of no further clarifying reduction. 'True,' along with its traditional transcendental associates, 'one,' 'beautiful,' and 'good,' is a reasonable candidate for such an irreducible status. Accordingly, we explicate 'true' by explaining the role it plays in language. It is a metalinguistic predicate which is properly predicated of propositions, or of sentences as used. To predicate 'true' of such a proposition is equivalent to asserting the proposition, or to judging that it should be asserted.

This explication clarifies what 'true' is predicated of and how it is predicated, but it does not yet explain why 'true' is so predicated. We might consider this by turning to Aristotle's classical formulation: "To say of what is that it is not, or of what is not that it is, is false; while to say of what is that it is or of what is not that it is not, is true."[10] Following Aristotle, this has often been taken as a definition of 'true' and 'false.' But I do not think it can consistently be accorded this role. If this expressed the *meaning* of 'true,' then it would be as contradictory to say that a proposition is true, though it does not correspond to reality, as it would be to say that someone is a bachelor, though he is married. Yet it is possible to affirm as true such ordinary sentences as "The sun rose at 5:33 this morning" or "If I were president I would declare a holiday" and such extraordinary sentences as theorems about transfinite numbers while either denying that they correspond to what is or wondering if there could possibly be anything for them to correspond to.

I am not rejecting Aristotle's statement. What I am rejecting is the attempt to use it as a definition. What it really expresses is the intentionality of a truth-claim. Focusing again on factual claims in ordinary language, our intention in asserting them is to state what is the case. Or, looking at the issue more abstractly, we are asserting a sort of isomorphism between a meaningful unit in a symbolic vehicle, language—the primary symbolic vehicle—and something extra-linguistic, a relation, state of affairs, or what have you. However, to add flesh to these bare bones it is necessary to explain what we mean by 'intentionality' and by language as a symbolic vehicle embodying a conceptual framework.

The role of 'true' as a metalinguistic predicate has been clarified by the role of judging as a mental act or of asserting as a linguistic performance. From the point of view of an analytic clarification, asserting is more basic than judging. We get at what a judgment is in terms of what results from a judgment, i.e., an assertion. More technically, just as a concept is explained as an inner word, i.e., its formal properties are understood by analogy with the corresponding words, so what a judgment is can be understood by analogy with the act of affirming or asserting a proposition. If judgment is taken as basic, the introduction of intentionality presents no problem, for we are already speaking of mental acts. But if we are speaking of linguistic performances, the category of intentionality may seem inappropriate, may seem to focus more on the subjective act of saying something rather than on the objective content of what is said. How can intentionality be clarified in this context?

We can, I believe, make an initial distinction between objective and subjective intentionality. Consider what would be involved in a description, or the specification of the rules, of a game such as chess or checkers. The description would specify certain moves as constituting a win, others as constituting a loss, while others are labeled a 'tie.' This is much like specifying the type of moves on a dance floor that constitute a waltz or a twist. But there is one difference between the two cases that such a syntactical description does not bring out. The operative intention in playing a game is to win. This is not simply a question of the subjective intention a particular player happens to have. It is objective in the sense that this intention is part of the meaning of the terms used. One who does not have the intention of winning cannot be said to be playing the game.[11]

'Assert' has an objective intentionality in a similar way. To say that a proposition is asserted rather than simply stated, or proposed, or conjectured, objectively presupposes a certain intention on the part of the asserter. Unless that intention is there, at least putatively, 'assert' is inappropriate. What is the intention in question? In an ordinary language factual claim, the objective intention must include stating what is the case. Or, in Aristotle's terms, saying of what is that it is.

Let's look at this a bit more abstractly. To label such a factual proposition as "true" is to assert that what is said corresponds to what is. What is said, the proposition, is a sentence playing a role. Its meaningfulness depends both on the meaning of the individual terms used and on their interrelation in a particular sentence as used in a definite context. In reporting a fact or describing a state of affairs, we construct an analog in a symbolic vehicle which is intended to represent the fact or state of affairs in question. The correspondence between a particular statement and what it is intended to represent will depend on the relation between language as a whole and reality as a whole. Quine's striking summary: "Our statements about the external world face the tribunal of sense experience not individually but only as a corporate body,"[12] may manifest an excessive reliance on the role of sense experience. But his stress on the system, rather than the individual sentence as the ultimate unit of meaning, is surely well founded.

This general consideration might seem to suggest an obvious strategy. If we first determine the relation between language as a whole and reality as a whole, then we have a general framework within which we can specify the relation between individual propositions and particular aspects of reality. Unfortunately, as Wittgenstein and others have pointed out, it is not possible to express in language the logical form which language shares with the world. Or, in epistemological terms, any attempt to specify the relation between language as a whole and reality as a whole presupposes a vantage point apart from both, a spectator view of both knowledge and reality. Such a celestial box seat is simply not available to you or me or anyone who is part of the human show. Language is the vehicle through which reality becomes revealed for us. To clarify the meaningfulness of a proposition and its adequacy as an analog, we must focus on the middle ground rather than the ultimate foundations of language. That is, we must examine the presuppositions, framework features, and logical entailments on which the meaningfulness of a proposition depends.

II

Truth and Conceptual Frameworks

This is beginning to sound too formal and abstract. Let us consider a couple of concrete examples. Suppose we could carry on a conversation with a member of a different and more primitive culture, e.g., an ancient Babylonian. He might report a metereological phenomenon by saying, "En-lil roared," where we would report the same phenomenon by saying, "It thundered." Confronted with a case of epileptic seizure he might report it by claiming, "The devil possessing Amil is shaking his soul." The question is: Should we accept his statements as true or false?

We, judging his conceptual framework from without, can readily make some obvious distinctions. His statements could be considered true if they are accepted simply as observation reports. If, however, he is intending to affirm the real existence of roaring sky gods and wrestling devils, we would not accept them as true. Now, let's suppose that our Babylonian, presumably an ordinary language Babylonian, attempted to make the same distinctions. What would he say? To say "En-lil roared, but there really is no En-lil" is to utter a contradiction. In no language is such an explicit contradiction a meaningful statement. If the language of devil possession is the only means linguistically available for reporting epileptic seizures, then to deny that a man in epileptic shock is possessed by the devil is to deny the clear testimony of one's own senses. The Babylonian, accordingly, cannot specify from within his own linguistic framework the degree to which in affirming a proposition he is also affirming the ontological and conceptual presuppositions on which the meaningfulness of the proposition depends. Yet, in neither case would he hesitate to assert the propositions or to label them true. From his point of view a truth-claim must be considered an intentional absolute embedded in a conceptual relative.

But we do not have these problems, because we could make

the distinctions that he was unable to make and specify the precise sense in which his propositions should be considered true. Yet in doing this we are operating within our own conceptual framework. Could later philosophers, as far removed from us as we are from the Babylonians, make similar distinctions concerning our assertions? I don't really believe that we will have to wait three thousand years for an answer. Living, as we do, in a complex, highly developed culture, we are aware of different conceptual frameworks which are partially competing and partially complementary.

Let us consider another simple example. "This drape is red." No one who is not color-blind would have any hesitation about labeling this true while labeling false any claims to the effect that it is green, or blue, or yellow. But how much are we actually asserting in this claim? A physicist, for example, might claim that the redness is explained in terms of the electromagnetic vibrations reflected from the drape. Suppose he attempts to resolve this science-common sense conflict by saying that the drape is not *really* red; it just looks red, a ploy that has been developed in different ways by both classical empiricists and by some contemporary analysts. The difficulty with this ploy becomes apparent when one tries to analyze what it means to say that something *looks* red. White paper, seen under pure red light, looks red. That is, it looks the way red things look when seen under normal circumstances. More generally, the concept of something looking x presupposes the concept of something being x. Our ordinary language is committed to the objective reality of such proper sensibles, or secondary qualities, as colors, sounds, tastes, smells, and feels. To use this language in making observation reports while simultaneously denying the objective validity of the category terms used to make the reports is to entangle oneself in the same type of contradiction that confounded our poor putative Babylonian.

The situation, however, is not hopeless. We can formulate the problem only because we are aware of competing conceptualizations. A clearer awareness of the role such conceptual frameworks play may afford a means of resolving the problem. But to do this we must first make explicit some of the basic features of our own conceptual framework, one shaped by and transmitted through ordinary language. This cannot be done, of course, by looking at our conceptual framework from without, but it can be done, at least in part, by analyzing the conditions of the possibility of meaningful intersubjective discourse. Rather than attempt an independent development, we shall simply summarize Strawson's analysis.[13]

Language cannot function as a means of interpersonal communication unless it can be used to refer to particulars which both the speaker and the hearer can identify. In some cases particulars are identified relative to other particulars (the assassin of Martin Luther King) or to special contexts, e.g., a story or an historical situation. But such relative identification presupposes basic particulars which are not identified in a relative way. This, in turn, is only possible if one can reidentify some basic particulars as objects, situations, locations, etc., previously encountered. A tacit, but necessary, presupposition of such reidentification is the perdurance in existence of objects even when not encountered, a perdurance of localized, relatively mobile objects which serves as the basis of a common space-time framework. The speaker's localization of himself with respect to such a framework serves as the anchor for identification of and reference to other objects and persons.

Before continuing this analysis, we should forestall some possible misunderstandings. What was summarized in the preceding paragraph was not an exposition of what objects must be in themselves. It was, rather, a clarification of how objects must be represented in language if language is to serve as a vehicle of interpersonal communication. 'Must' is a strong term, connoting the contention that any language which can serve as a vehicle of interpersonal communication is necessarily centered around the same conceptual core. Strawson and others feel that such strong claims are justified, since the analysis was not geared to our language but to the conditions of the possibility of any language which can serve as a vehicle for meaningful interpersonal communication, i.e., it is not necessarily valid for the type of artificial languages constructed by the logicians.

In my opinion this contention is a bit too strong. Strawson's analysis, a significant contribution to contemporary philosophy, was conducted by a process of asking and answering questions. One could carry his type of questioning a step further and ask about the conditions of the possibility of a Strawsonian analysis. The basic condition is that the questions asked be meaningful in our conceptual framework. If there were a language with a conceptual core radically different from ours, then one using this language to perform a Strawsonian analysis would presumably ask rather different questions.

Nevertheless, his method of analysis does make explicit the conceptualization of reality implicit in our language. The resulting descriptive metaphysics may be summarized as follows. The world is an interrelated collection of mobile, relatively enduring objects. These exist as substances endowed with both primary and secondary qualities. The interrelation of these objects through proximity and activity supplies the framework for a general spatio-temporal ordering. Persons, and, in a modified derivative way, animals, constitute among objects a unique irreducible class of which both physical and mental predicates are attributable. Among persons I have a unique role. My bodily location anchors the spatio-temporal framework for me and serves as the zero-point or center in relating myself to this world of interrelated objects and persons.

This descriptive metaphysics is not something we learn *in addition to* learning a language. One cannot learn to apply terms to objects without learning what sorts of terms apply to what sorts of objects, or the way language categorizes reality. Language cannot be used to refer, describe, explain, or narrate without implicitly using a conceptualization of reality. Labeling a proposition 'true' is equivalent to endorsing it as a candidate for affirmation. To what extent is one also endorsing the descriptive metaphysics used to frame the proposition? This question, I believe, does not admit of a precise answer. One cannot use a categorization of reality to assert a fact and simultaneously call into question the validity of the categorization employed. Any assessment of the validity of the conceptualization employed presupposes that one has a different and superior conceptualization which is used as the basis for judgment. From within a given conceptual framework, a proposition affirmed as true has the status of an intentional absolute embedded in a conceptual relative.

Perhaps the significance of this can be seen more clearly if we return to the example we agreed to accept as true. Consider the following sentences:

(1) The drape is red.

(2) The quality designated by 'red' inheres in the substance denoted by the referential unit 'this drape.'

(3) The light reflected by the surface molecules in this drape is about 6,500 Angstrom units.

Sentence (1) uses a descriptive metaphysics to make an observation report. (2) goes beyond this in explicitly affirming this implicit metaphysics. (3) tries to explain the fact reported in (1) by using a conceptualization of reality, at least of this aspect of reality, different from that implicit in ordinary language. (2) is compatible with (1); it might even be said to be conceptually entailed by (1), a type of conceptual entailment that is basic to a metaphysics of common sense realism. Yet it is possible, indeed common, for the person affirming (1) as true to reject (2) as an explanation while accepting (3). In such a split acceptance the truth claim implicit in (1) is minimal. It is intended as an observation report, not as an ontological claim.

This conclusion suggests a facile resolution of the problem we have been considering. The intentionality of the speaker determines and delimits the precise significance, or the ontic boundaries, implicit in the proposition he affirms. Intentionality, however, does not function in so absolute a manner. *We* could distinguish between different intentions that could be present in the affirmation of (1) because alternative conceptual frameworks were available to us. What if the original speaker knew nothing of such alternatives, were conceptually confined to an ordinary language framework. *He* could say that he intended (1) merely as an observation report, but not as an ontic commitment, only by claiming that in affirming that the drape is red he did not intend to say that it is *really* red. Though intentionality is not reducible to a set of rules for the use of language, the categories that language makes available serve to specify one's operative intentionality.

It may seem that we have painted ourselves into a corner. In affirming proposition (1) while denying (2), we may seem to be claiming that (1) is true though it does not correspond to reality. One facile solution, which does not leave tracks in the paint, is to say that in affirming (1) what we really mean is that any normal truthful observer seeing this drape under standard conditions would make an equivalent report about its color. But this will not work. Sentence (1) is not about observers and their reactions; it is about bodies and their properties. Hence, it does seem to entail (2), the sentence we are denying. Is this inconsistent?

Not necessarily. We could say that (2) is conceptually entailed by (1) only by considering language when it is idling, rather than when it is functioning. Its function in the present instance is to report an observational fact. The difficulty here comes from a misuse of the correspondence theory of truth, the type of misuse that has so often shored up naive realism. The argument, or at least a simplistic version of it, would run as follows. Proposition (1) is true. It could not be true unless what it says corresponds to what is. Therefore the object in question must have a real act of existence and must be endowed with the properties we attribute to it. From the truth of a proposition one deduces the objective ontological determination that is the necessary condition of its being true.

Such arguments, I believe, ultimately rest on a misinterpretation of the functioning of language. 'Red' is the type of term called a 'resemblance class predicate.'[14] To learn to use such terms properly one must have the ability to make the appropriate sensory discriminations, i.e., see the difference between red and blue. One must also have absorbed basic syntactic structures and semantic categories. This means an operative, rather than a formal, knowledge that 'red' functions as a predicate, that it is a property of material objects rather than of ideas, events, processes, etc. Granted such a sensitive and intellectual basis, one absorbs the proper use of the term by hearing it predicated of standard members (roses are red) and denied of standard non-members (violets are not red). This sets a resemblance class. Objects that are perceived to be like the standard members in this respect, e.g., sunsets, lipstick, etc., should be called 'red.' Such a resemblance class inevitably has fuzzy borders.

Calling 'true' the proposition, "This drape is red," is roughly equivalent to affirming it. One is justified in affirming it if he has a reflective grasp of evidence sufficient to warrant assent. This involves some reflective awareness of the presuppositions, both linguistic and ontological, implicit in the proposition affirmed. But this reflective awareness is functional rather than philosophical. One must know how to use the language; one need not know how to analyze it. Using it in the present instance involves being able to give a correct answer to the question, "What color is this drape?" Pre-judgmental reflection must grasp in an interrelated way: the meaning of the question asked; the logic of color terms, a logic that presupposes the prior assimilation of the syntactical and semantical rules governing the application of resemblance-class predicates; and the relevant perceptual discrimination.

The reply, a warranted assent, *uses* a conceptualization of reality, but does not affirm it. But neither does it deny it. The functional utility of the conceptualization was presupposed rather than questioned. To question it one must render it explicit by thematizing it and then inquire into its validity. The functional utility of a descriptive metaphysics in framing observation reports is not in itself sufficient evidence to warrant asserting its truth in a correspondence sense.

The fact that a proposition is reasonably judged to be true need not imply that it is explanatory in any profound sense. Yet, we do wish to give explanations, to gain a more profound understanding of the reality affirmed through our true propositions. How attempts to do this, to go beyond the limitations and functional utility of ordinary language, relate to the problem of truth will be our concern in subsequent lectures. Perhaps we can summarize the analysis of 'true' developed in this lecture by comparing it with the theories of truth and clarifications of 'true' considered in the first lecture.

III
SUMMARY AND COMPARISON

The most obvious parallel is with the assertive-redundancy analysis of 'true' suggested by Ramsey and developed by Strawson. According to this view, labeling a proposition 'true' is roughly equivalent to affirming it. The equivalence is not complete. Where "Snow is white" is about objects and their properties, the further claim, "'Snow is white' is true," is directly about a proposition and only indirectly about material objects. Also, the latter formulation is a bit more solemn, not to say pompous, and implicitly presupposes that the validity of the former claim has been called into question.

Granted such Austinian qualifications, there is nevertheless an equivalence. 'True' is clarified by the role it plays in language. Its role, as a predicate proper to propositions, parallels the role of assertion, considered as a linguistic performance. One learns to use 'true' properly by learning both to assert and to speak about propositions. These aspects of the A-R analysis have been accepted and incorporated into the present treatment.

The basic difficulty with the A-R clarification is the narrowness of its scope. Strawson himself admits this. After listing some of the problems which any theory of truth must consider he states: "Under the general title *Truth* all these matters have, by one philosopher or another, been discussed; and since the Ramsey-like account of the word 'true' is rather thin fare, it would seem somewhat of a pity that so notable a title should be reserved for so unexciting a thesis. Better, perhaps, let the theory of truth become, as it has shown so pronounced a historical tendency to become, part of some other theory: that of knowledge; or of mind; or of meaning."[15] The A-R analysis serves as a necessary point of departure for coming to grips with the more interesting issues, but does not itself treat them. Hence, we must move to a consideration of the problems posed by the more ambitious theories of truth.

The correspondence theory of truth certainly makes some interesting claims. But many of its formulations also entail a certain amount of confusion. What Aristotle gave was essentially an analytical clarification of 'true' and 'false.' In this sense one is certainly justified in saying that a factual proposition is true when it states what is the case and false when it states what is not the case. But this correspondence with reality is essentially functional. Language usage involves descriptive conventions specifying which sorts of terms are correlated with which sorts of objects, properties, situations, or whatever. Such descriptive conventions serve to focus our manner of specifying objects, referring to them, and predicating properties of them. Both reference and correspondence are internal to a linguistic framework. Within this framework their usage is clarified by the functions they fulfill rather than by metaphysical arguments that may be adduced to support them.

Correspondence theorists have rarely confined themselves to these limitations. There is an abiding temptation to read into 'correspondence' a significance that transcends the limitations of the framework within which it functions. A proposition that is true and known to be true must, it is argued, correspond to what is the case in reality. Hence, the argument continues, by analyzing what a proposition says we can determine what reality is. This is essentially a *modus tollendo tollens* argument. If the object itself did not objectively have the property attributed to it then the proposition attributing this property would be false. But it is not false. Therefore the object must have this property as an objective ontological determination of its mode of existence. And therefore, by implication, a metaphysics of substance and properties is justified.

This argument ultimately rests on a consideration of language when it is idling rather than when it is functioning. An analysis that does not presuppose the myth of the given and treats language as a functioning system rather than a transparent medium inevitably entails a fuzzier idea of correspondence. The correspondence implicitly affirmed in asserting a factual proposition is a correspondence between a proposition, a functioning unit in a symbolic vehicle, and something extra-linguistic, a situation or state of affairs. The meaning of this proposition, or the way the sentence used functions, depends both upon the syntactical rules that give language its functioning unification and on the conceptualization of reality implicit in the language. From within a linguistic framework it is impossible to specify the precise degree to which, in asserting a proposition, one also affirms the presuppositions, framework features, and conceptual entailments which condition the meaningfulness of the proposition. The ontic commitments of the affirmed proposition fade away from a focal illumination on the fact asserted through a penumbral haze of implicit pre-suppositions to a shadowy background extending to the horizon of the speaker's intentionality-structure, the world for him.

Yet, in declaring a proposition true, there is a correspondence between what is said and what is clearly intended. The correspondence theory does make explicit the intentionality of a truth claim. An old song informs us that wishing will make it so. Would that this were true. But, unfortunately, one cannot argue *tout court* from the intention of stating what is the case to the ontological structure of the reality intended. A more pedantic and painstaking analysis is required in assessing the manner in which and the degree to which this intention is fulfilled.

In such an assessment the coherence and pragmatic theories of truth supply some necessary criteria. We do not accept the basic contention of the coherence theory: that to say a judgment is true is to say that it coheres with other judgments already accepted as true. What we do get from this theory are necessary but not sufficient internal conditions for accepting a particular proposition as true. We should distinguish between the role this type of criterion plays in an ordinary language framework and in a formal language. In ordinary language the crucial point is not so much the coherence of a proposition with other individual propositions, but with framework features of the language system. A proposition cannot be judged true unless it is first meaningful. A necessary but not sufficient condition for such meaningfulness is that it be consonant with such basic framework features as the syntactical rules that make a collection of words into a sentence and the semantic categories which specify the way in which this language may be used to describe, or explain, or narrate.

This may seem like a purely grammatical criterion until one reflects on the role it plays in the advancement of thought. Within a prescientific ordinary language framework, there is no meaningful way to say that this paper is not really white. It cannot be said because it is not coherent with the rules governing semantic categories in this framework. Yet, if there is to be any advance in a theory of color or light, it must be said somehow. A framework that does not permit such statements must be changed. And so the requirement of coherence not only sets a necessary condition for meaningfulness. Whenever it blocks the path of inquiry, it ultimately serves to generate a dialectical development leading to new specialized frameworks with somewhat different functions.

Coherence requirements play a more significant role in formal language systems. In a deductive system, for example, statements must be interconnected by some process of logical entailment. The problems this engenders will be considered in the next lecture.

In mentioning the pragmatic aspects of truth, I should begin with a linguistic clarification. I am using the term 'pragmatic' in a way that the founders of pragmatism—or, for that matter, anyone else—might find hard to recognize. What I have actually been using in considering these problems is a synthesis (of sorts) of Bernard Lonergan's theory of judgment, a pragmatic theory of acceptance, derived chiefly from Quine and Sellars, and Dewey's stress on the role of inquiry.

There are two aspects of this that I wish to consider, internal and external judgments, where the terms are used in Carnap's sense depending on whether one is speaking within or about a conceptual system.[16] The problem of internal judgment is concerned with the transition from a proposition proposed as a hypothesis to a proposition asserted as true. Consider, for example, Pasteur's hypothesis that small living forms, such as maggots, are not spontaneously generated but arise only by generation from other living beings, a hypothesis that went contrary to the accepted opinions of his day. It is customary— and certainly correct in a sense—to say that he affirmed this hypothesis as true when he had evidence sufficient to warrant assent.

But this simple claim does not get to the heart of the problem. Others, who understood the meaning of the hypothesis and were confronted with the same evidence, might not, and, as a matter of historical fact, often did not, affirm the proposition as true. Evidence of itself does not compel assent. It supplies a motive for assent only if it is *understood* as sufficient.

Here, I believe, Lonergan makes an essential contribution with his insistence on understanding what it is to understand and his analysis of different types of understanding. In the reflective understanding grounding affirmation, we must understand both the proposition presented as a candidate for affirmation and also the relations between this proposition, that of which it is affirmed, and the reasons because of which it is affirmed. The mode of understanding operative here is something irreducible. It cannot be reduced, as many would like, to a logical relation between statements reporting evidence and the statement affirmed as a conclusion.

Rather than attempt to expound this view here by transposing Lonergan's development into a terminology and methodology that comes to grips with the linguistic problems involved in referring to mental acts and states,[17] I will simply consider what seems to me to be the decisive case, the problem of external judgment. Instead of simply judging the truth of a statement formulated within a given linguistic framework, it is occasionally necessary to judge between competing frameworks. This is particularly true in the case of scientific revolutions. If this judgment is thought of merely as an inner analog of a proposition, then one must ask which linguistic framework the proposition is in, that of the old theory or of the new one which seeks to replace it. A little reflection reveals that it cannot be either. A formal clarification of mental acts and states requires an analogy between aspects of speech and aspects of thought. A concept, for example, is spoken of as an inner word and the formal properties of concepts are understood by analogy with the formal properties of words. Nevertheless, thinking cannot be understood simply as an interior talking to oneself.

We do make such external judgments. Though simple observation, filtered through ordinary language, reveals that the sun rises and sets, we have little difficulty accepting as true an explanation of this observation in terms of the earth's rotation. Yet, this acceptance is reasonable and justifiable only if we accept the framework in which such an account is formulated as more basic than a common sense framework, more basic at least for the purpose of giving explanations of natural phenomena.

One could label this 'a pragmatic theory of acceptance' and stress the role of inquiry in seeking and appraising reasons sufficient to warrant such acceptance. Or one could label it 'judgment' and try to clarify the role of pre-judgmental reflection in motivating assent. Ideally, one should synthesize the two approaches, but this is not our task here. Regardless of the label affixed, one should recognize that making judgments about the truth of propositions or the acceptability of the framework in which they are embedded is something more than simply inferring conclusions by a process of logical deduction.

Robert Johann, last year's Hecker lecturer, is developing a doctrine which he calls "ontological pragmatism." Though my manner of doing philosophy is rather different from his, this label would fit the doctrine I have developed so far. The propositions that one judges to be true depend not just on facts, as an objective given, but on the framework in which the facts are reported. It is a little misleading to speak of *the basic framework*. Different type of frameworks can be considered basic depending on the purpose for which they are used: to describe experiences, relate events, clarify meanings, or give explanations. Each framework has ontic commitments: a specification of the type of entities accepted as basic and the sort of properties, activities, and relations that characterize these entities. What I am proposing is that the ontic commitments we accept as basic should depend on the frameworks we accept as explanatory. But more of this in the next lecture.

APPENDIX:

TRUTH IN AQUINAS AND HEIDEGGER

In the opinion of many, the two philosophers who have the most profound treatment of the problem of truth are Thomas Aquinas and Martin Heidegger. They are certainly the two most influential philosophers in contemporary Christian thought. My development of the problem of truth slights both of them, an omission that inevitably raises questions concerning the credibility and acceptability of my account. The omission, however, was more apparent than real. In developing the doctrine presented in this chapter, I did consider both authors and, though my knowledge of Heidegger is rather slight, was influenced by their views. What I wish to present here is the relation between their views, as I understand them, and my own development of the problem.

Though I lay no claim to being a Thomist—and, in fact, am not quite sure what such claims mean—the study of St. Thomas' writings has had a formative influence on my own philosophical development. The first two articles I wrote for publication—articles which discerning editors fortunately rejected—represented an attempt to synthesize St. Thomas' views on the grades of being and their interrelation. There is a Dominican adage, *"Thomas semper formalissime loquitur,"* which suggests a certain degree of caution in quoting Aquinas' theory of truth without first considering his ideas on the nature and function of a philosophical explanation. For this reason I wish to consider his ideas on the methodology of philosophical explanation before examining what he has to say on the nature of truth.[1]

St. Thomas, accepting and extending ideas derived from

Aristotle, thought of philosophy as involving a process of analysis and synthesis repeated at different levels. Analysis begins with the confused knowledge of ordinary experience and the language in which it is described (the *magis nota quoad nos*) and seeks to understand the beings of ordinary experience, i.e., material beings, by a resolution into principles of being. The principles sought were the inner constitutive principles of matter and form (together with the privation of form needed to explain change) and the extrinsic principles of efficient causality, or agency, and final causality, or purpose. After such principles have been attained, one can form a synthesis in which the first principles of explanation express the ultimate results of the process of analysis. Thus, explanation in the synthetic mode has an ordering (Thomas refers to it as the sapiential ordering) which is the reverse of that proper to the analytic mode. The facts and questions that launched the search for principles and were *first* in the analytic mode are now deduced from, or at least explained in terms of, the principles on which they depend, thereby becoming *last* in the synthetic mode.

This analysis and synthesis is part of the philosophy of nature, or physics in the Aristotelian sense, and is not yet metaphysics. It is the study of material being, but not of being as being. Metaphysics, strictly speaking, begins with the judgment of separation, the conclusion that all beings are not material beings.[2] Such a conclusion, again following Aristotle, comes at the end of the *Physics* with the conclusion that the First Mover cannot be a material being. It could also come with the conclusion that the human soul is immaterial. However, even though Thomas believed that Aristotle, his guide in philosophical methodology, held this opinion, he knew that there were other interpretations of Aristotle.

'Being' does not necessarily mean 'material being.' What, then, is being as being? The basic tool the metaphysician must rely on is logical analysis. St. Thomas is quite explicit on this. Both metaphysics and logic have a common subject, all being. Through the mediation of concepts, everything comes together in being and its essential attributes. Such concepts can be studied: either insofar as they express the reality of a thing, in which case one has metaphysics; or insofar as the mind has a certain way of relating one concept to another, in which case one has a science of the rules of predication. This Thomas calls 'logic,' though much of what he does under this heading would today be called 'linguistic analysis' or 'semantics.' The basic way of determining the manner in which a concept (or inner word) expresses the reality of a thing is by examining the way in which the term is used. Doig, whose analysis of Aquinas' doctrine we have been summarizing in this paragraph, draws the conclusion: "If the present study of Aquinas is correct, then it is impossible to overestimate the importance of the logical investigation of the *modus praedicandi*."[3]

Such a semantic analysis, indispensable as it is, is not an end in itself for the metaphysician. It is a tool functioning in the protracted process of causal analysis and synthesis. This metaphysical analysis, following the Thomistic program, terminates in the ultimate inner constitutive principles of being, essence and existence, and the ultimate extrinsic principle, God as the first cause and final end of all being.[4] The proper expression of these principles should serve as the starting point for a metaphysical synthesis. However, when Thomas attempted to write a synthesis, he wrote as a theologian rather than as a philosopher. His theological synthesis will be considered in Chapter IV. Here, I will only point out that it presupposes the ideas and methodology of a metaphysical synthesis and adds further formative ideas on God and his creation derived from Christian tradition.

Thomas' treatment of the problem of truth, his *De Veritate,* was written in the synthetic mode (or according to what Gilson calls the theological order). Thus, he begins his treatment by saying that 'true' is a transcendental attribute of being[5] and that the truth of a being is primarily its correspondence with the divine mind.[6] This clearly presupposes that a doctrine of being and God has already been developed.

Relying on the *De Veritate* as well as on other writings of St. Thomas, it is possible to summarize his doctrine of truth as it is explained in the *synthetic mode*. God is truth. Things are true by virtue of their conformity to the divine mind, or the exemplary ideas in accord with which they were created.[7] The human mind can possess truth by virtue of its proximate conformity to things and its ultimate conformity to the divine mind. This conformity is affirmed only in a judgment. The human mind, accordingly, posits truth only through a judgment.

A judgment is the affirmation of the conformity (or lack of conformity) between the inner word *(verbum mentale)* that is stated and that of which it is stated. This conformity is grasped in reflection preceding judgment, a reflection that involves a conversion to the phantasm and an awareness of what the soul (or mind) is as a knower. Truth and error would not both be possible unless the inner word affirmed in judgment (which follows the first mental operation, simple apprehension) were complex, allowing of both composition and division. Thus, to use Thomas' example, man and white are the same in the subject (a white man) but differ in idea. One mentally divides what is objectively one and then composes the corresponding terms in the form of a proposition, "The man is white." In this proposition, the subject stands for the supposit and the predicate is attached to the subject but predicated of the supposit for which the subject stands, i.e., the man is white but 'the man' is not white.

An affirmed proposition, accordingly, involves a double composition. First, there is the composition of subject and predicate forming the proposition, or complex inner word. Secondly, there is the composition of the proposition and its affirmation, something symbolized in contemporary logic by |—, Frege's affirmation sign. Or, as Thomas put it: "To this diversity in idea there corresponds the plurality of predicate and subject, while the intellect signifies the identity of the thing by the composition itself."[8] An affirmed proposition is a truth-claim. One can make this explicit by quoting the proposition and predicating 'true' of it. This is simply a different way of asserting the proposition. There is no need to read Strawson's A-R analysis back into Thomas' thought. It is already explicit in his writings: "But 'true' and 'false' add nothing to the significance of assertoric propositions; for there is the same significance in 'Socrates runs' and 'it is true that Socrates runs' and in 'Socrates is not running' and 'it is false that Socrates is running.'"[9]

Thus, in the order of synthesis, the Thomistic explanation of truth begins with God and terminates with a clarification of the syntactical features (relation of subject and predicate in a proposition), semantic roles (relation of subject and predicate to supposit), and performative aspects (what one does with words in asserting a proposition) of propositions accepted as true. This is the proper order when one proceeds from the *priora quoad se* (provided one accepts what Thomas has to say concerning what is prior in reality). The order of analysis should be the reverse of this.

These methodological strictures are little noted and rarely observed. Thus, many introductions to metaphysics, written in accord with what is, fortunately, a fading tradition, demonstrate the authenticity of their Thomism by an extensive use of citations from Thomas' synthetic works. But the exploitation of such texts for explanatory purposes inevitably involves a disregard of the methodology Thomas thought essential to philosophical development. Following such a methodological ordering is not simply a pedagogical device; it plays an essentia: role in conditioning one's philosophical understanding. Thomas explains this in terms of a distinction between a *'positio,'* a conclusion simply stated as a proposition, and a *'via,'* the reasoning process by which this conclusion is obtained or explained. The two together constitute a formal philosophical treatment, but a *positio* by itself is not really a proper part of philosophy.[10]

My own ideas on philosophical methodology were conditioned by but differ from those developed by St. Thomas. I accept the idea of philosophical explanation as a process of analysis preceding and, hopefully, leading to a synthesis. But Thomas' method of analysis, e.g., the type of questions he asked and the manner in which he asked them, manifests implicit presuppositions about knowing and being which cannot now be accepted as unproblematic. For him the universe was an ordered whole constituted of beings whose specific natures and essential interrelations were forever fixed. Knowing involved the intellect's becoming the thing known, i.e., an identity in the intentional order between the nature of the thing known and the form *(species intelligibilis impressa)* impressed on the passive intellect. Speech, both the inner word *(species intelligibilis expressa)* and the spoken word, are intelligible and meaningful by virtue of the fact that they express the 'whatness' and thus reflect the intelligibility of the thing known. Though material in nature, speech participates in the intelligibility of the intentional order.

If a doctrine of meaning were erected on this foundation, one would inevitably, I believe, reach the conclusion that the meaning of a term is derivative from the meaning of a concept, while the meaning of a concept depends on its relation to an object (or the 'whatness' of an object), a relation of identity in the intentional order. This theory of meaning is quite explicit in Aristotle and its acceptance serves to structure the type of semantic analysis Thomas relies on: "Spoken words are the symbols of mental experience and written words are the symbols of spoken words. Just as all men have not the same writing, so all men have not the same speech sounds, but the mental experiences, which these directly symbolize, are the same for all, as also are those things of which our experiences are the images."[11]

Thus the meaning of a term, at least of a substantive term, is, for St. Thomas, essentially a thing-term relation achieved through the mediation of inner mental states. This is, in contemporary jargon, a private language theory. One of the most significant contributions of Wittgenstein's *Philosophical In-*

vestigations[12] was his probing analysis of private language theories. An idea, which I accept, stemming from the *Investigations* is that the meaning of a term is essentially public and only derivatively private. Meaning, accordingly, is clarified by an analysis of the role a term plays in language, rather than as a relation between a term and an object.[13] Acceptance of this thesis undercuts much of the methodology basic to the Aristotelian-Scholastic tradition of analysis, e.g., getting at constitutive principles of beings by analyzing the concepts we use to express these beings. This does not necessarily imply that the conclusions Thomas reached are wrong. But it does imply that the rationale of justification he employed (or at least reflected—his philosophical analyses occur chiefly in his commentaries on the works of Aristotle) is inadequate in the light of contemporary critical standards. Hence the need for a critical redevelopment of philosophy, a redevelopment that begins with a probing analysis and aspires to a new synthesis.

In spite of these qualifications on doctrine and method, I believe that the view presented here is generally compatible with the doctrine that one would have if he developed Thomas' theory of truth in the analytic mode and stopped short of the judgment of separation and the development of metaphysics. I am not opposed to the idea of developing a metaphysics, though I have not yet done so myself. But the dividing line separating the type of analytically developed, consistent conceptualization of reality (which I would substitute for his philosophy of nature) and a metaphysics of being is not his judgment of separation; rather it is the critical problem, the question of whether this, or any conceptualization of reality, represents things as they are in themselves.[14]

Martin Heidegger's theory of truth presents a more formidable problem due to the complexity of his thought and the tortured language through which it is expressed, and due also to the fact that my understanding of his philosophy is rather superficial.[15] With Heidegger, as with any original systematic philosopher, a distinctive methodology of development conditions the intelligibility of the doctrines developed. Heidegger himself is quite insistent on this point.[16] Accordingly, after indicating the general thrust of his philosophical development, we shall try to outline the process of analysis by means of which he arrives at his distinctive conclusions on the nature of truth.

His basic purpose is to question the meaning of being. His method is phenomenological, which he interprets in the radical sense of letting that which shows itself be seen as it is. The basic phenomenon he lets be seen in *Being and Time* is *Dasein,* considered as "there-being," that being in whom the Being-process can reveal itself. Through phenomenological analysis, *Dasein* reveals itself as finite transcendence whose ultimate meaning is time.

The idea of letting that which manifests itself be seen as it is inevitably involves the problem of truth: not simply the meaning of 'true' but an analysis of the grounds of the possibility of truth. In accord with his methodology, Heidegger gets at this by beginning with the phenomenon of truth, that which has appeared as truth in Western thought, in the hope that the phenomenon properly seen will reveal its own *logos.*

The phenomenon of truth is encapsulated in the phrase *"adequatio intellectus et rei."* Truth, as it has appeared in Western thought, is the conformity of a proposition to reality, of what is said to that of which it is said. This tradition reached its focal point in medieval Scholasticism, e.g., in the Thomistic theory of truth. Thanks to a theological background, supplying the notion that what things are corresponds to ideas in the mind of God, the medievals could speak of both the truth of judgments, or logical truths, and the truth of things, or ontological truth. This way of viewing the problem perdured in Western thought even when the theological presuppositions grounding it faded away.

The difficulty with this approach, as Heidegger sees it, is that it presupposes that we already know what an object is, what a judgment is, and what it means for the two to correspond.

One way of questioning these presuppositions is to inquire into the conditions of the possibility of the traditional notion of truth. Correspondence of any sort presupposes a contextual totality in which it is possible for two things to relate, a type of totality that is not had when one thinks of truth as a relationship between a thought and a thing, or an ideal and a real object. The context of truth must be the immediate presence of judgments to things. The basic function of judgment, accordingly, is to render things accessible, a work more of discovery than of description. The presupposition of such discovery is *Dasein's* radical openness to being, something that must be understood in terms of man's mode of being in the world.

Philosophers in general, and truth theorists in particular, have focused on knowledge, conceptual and propositional knowledge, as man's most fundamental way of encountering the world of beings. But such knowledge presupposes and emerges out of a more fundamental level of encounter through activity. *Dasein,* concerned with the care and management of things as the means of his self-realization, encounters objects in the world as instruments to be manipulated or used in achieving his purposes. The being of these things is concealed by their availability as instruments functioning as part of an instrumental complex. A hammer is understood, not by contemplating it, but by hammering with it. The world is encountered as the fundamental workshop. There is a sort of conformity here, since man must adapt his activities to the properties and inter-relationships of bodies. But this adaptation is noetically characterized by concern with the use and management of things to achieve purposes, a concern that distracts man from the beingness of things.

How does an instrument come to reveal itself as an object, or, in epistemological terms, what are the conditions for the emergence of judgment as a discovery of being? Heidegger's answer is: through breakdown and beauty. The instrument that ceases to function draws attention to itself as a being. Its breakdown ruptures the operational context of the lived world, makes *Dasein* aware of the instrument as a being, and of himself as a knower rather than just a doer. Other forms of breakdown are: psychological disillusion, or the breakdown of a life, and theoretical contradiction, or the breakdown of a system. Ordinarily it is only during periods of conceptual revolution that scientists reflect on the nature of their discipline, or let a science manifest itself, through human consciousness, as what it is.

Beauty has a similar effect in letting an object stand forth as what it is. We do not notice the marble in the stairs we tread on. But Michaelangelo's David lets appear what marble can be and do and become. Such moments of revelation are necessarily fleeting. The broken instrument ceases to be an object of contemplation and becomes material for repair. The familiar art object blends into the background. Only through systematic retrieval can one recapture such moments and attempt to get back to the ground of being. So truth, or the discovery of being, is necessarily characterized by a negativity, the ruptured context of relations that lets an object appear as a being, the forgetfulness of being that precedes and follows the moment of revelation.

The ground of truth lies in *Dasein's* capacity to let things be what they are. When they appear man can let these things serve as the criteria of his thoughts and conduct. By letting what reveals itself be and by letting thought conform to things, man achieves the phenomenon of truth. The capacity to do this must be the ultimate ground of truth. Hence, Heidegger concludes, truth is in essence freedom.[17] But this freedom is not something which man possesses. Rather, it is something which possesses man: "Freedom, so understood as the letting-be of what-is, fulfills and perfects the nature of truth in the sense that truth is the unconcealment and revelation of what-is."[18]

This foundational analysis began as a way back to the ground of metaphysics. It eventually led to an attempt to overcome metaphysics, on the grounds that all metaphysics seeks to transcend, rather than accept, man's finiteness and temporality. What is one to make of such an analysis? Carnap dismissed Heidegger by pointing out that *"Das Nicht nichtet"* violates normal syntax. Positivists and analysts have generally ignored and sometimes ridiculed his writings. A rejection not based on critical understanding has no philosophical significance. Yet, one gets the unmistakable impression that what Heidegger is saying, or attempting to say, violates the "No Trespassing" signs that analysts have set up to mark the boundaries of meaningful language.

I have no intention of attempting to pass judgment on the validity of Heidegger's thought. What I would like to do is to indicate the relation between what I am doing in these lectures and what, as I understand it, he has done. In his terminology, the present analysis is concerned with a clarification of the phenomenon of truth. It focuses on the meaning of 'true,' the criteria of its applicability, the significance and relative success of attempts to say what is true. But it does not get down to the ultimate grounds of the possibility of truth.

If, however, one does want to make such an ultimate analysis, something I am not now prepared to attempt, then the type of preliminary analysis presented here is, I believe, a necessary prerequisite. This is not only for the reasons Heidegger himself cites, the importance of achieving an adequate natural conception of the world, or letting the phenomena appear.[19] It is also because such an analysis can supply norms for the meaningful extension of language to new domains in which one wishes to affirm true propositions. Such norms are of crucial significance for the type of foundational investigation that phenomenologists in general, and Heidegger in particular, are attempting.

Husserl introduced the idea of *bracketing,* of suspending the natural viewpoint to return to the things themselves as given in immediate experience. Heidegger, Merleau-Ponty and other phenomenologists, who have either departed from or attempted to go beyond Husserl's thought, have retained some form of bracketing and return to immediate preconceptual experience as an essential part of the phenomenological method. Any attempt to do this inevitably involves a process of asking questions and seeking answers, of describing experiences and analyzing their presuppositions and conditions. Language is the basic and indispensable tool of phenomenological analysis.

The language used implicitly contains a descriptive metaphysics, a conceptualization of reality which serves to categorize the items referred to, to specify the type of predicates that can be attributed to them, and the type of reports that can be made about them. What the phenomenologists present is not the preconceptual given of immediate experience, but a language-dependent thematization of this given—or of a theory of what this given must be like. The natural standpoint is not, and cannot be, completely suspended. It implicitly functions through the language used to develop phenomenology.

What can be done about this? An attempt to push the bracketing further so as to remove this aspect of the natural standpoint, or an attempt to deny the role that such language-dependent conceptualization plays, backs one into some strange and untenable views of language and meaning. Either one holds that the meaning of the key terms used is had from the experiences these terms refer to, the term-thing concept of meaning discussed and dismissed earlier, or one seeks some language, or primeval *logos,* in reality prior to and grounding the meaningfulness of language as spoken.[20] Both approaches obscure rather than explain the problem at issue.

Another possible strategm is to admit that bracketing is incomplete, that the language used to describe and reconstruct immediate experience necessarily thematizes by the imposition of conceptual categories, yet claim that the program can still work. Thus one would claim that such thematization is the medium through which the phenomena appear. If one goes beyond reading phenomenological accounts and actually practices the phenomenological method, then he will attain a privileged access to his own immediate experience. What really counts, then, are the phenomena that let themselves be seen rather than the medium through which one is nudged out of his distractedness and forgetfulness of being. Or, in Heidegger's terms, judgment is essentially revelatory rather than descriptive, and the capacity to do this constitutes *Dasein:* "The Being of truth is connected primordially with Dasein. And only because Dasein is as constituted by disclosedness (that is, by understanding), can anything like Being be understood; only so is it possible to understand Being."[21] This is essentially an adaptation of Aristotle's argument (for the possible intellect) that whatever it is that renders things accessible as they are cannot have an determinate character of its own. But things become accessible through *Dasein's* questioning and responding, analyzing and describing—and language does have a determinate character of its own. This strategm leads from phenomenology to obscurantism or mysticism, using language as a means of rendering present the ineffable.

A facile conclusion, and one that is effectively operative in making the English channel an almost insurmountable philosophical barrier, is to say that the phenomenological tradition is essentially misguided. What they are trying to do simply cannot be done. I am inclined to believe that what they are trying to do *must* be done if philosophy is to realize its proper function. But doing it in a critically acceptable way involves a redevelopment of phenomenological methodology. Before suspending the natural viewpoint one must first explicitate it. Such an explicitation should clarify the role that language plays in thematizing and describing, including describing immediate experience. It should also supply criteria which allow one to distinguish between using a categorization to report experience and implicitly affirming the categorization employed. Finally, by examining the process of language extension and transformation that has proven most successful, i.e., the natural sciences, it should supply norms for the meaningful extension of language to new domains. Any attempt to suspend the natural viewpoint necessarily entails a language dependent excursion into new domains. In short, the type of analytic account attempted in these lectures, however inadequate its execution may be, is a necessary prerequisite to the development of a phenomenological account that admits of a critical justification.

III

TRUTH
IN SCIENCE

In the first lecture we gave a brief historical overview of the relation between theories of truth and the philosophical problems involved in interpreting scientific systems. It was a story of sharp contrasts and polar reversals. Yet there was a rather surprising core of agreement on some basic strategy arguments. This stemmed from the consideration that scientific theories seem to have such a formal deductive structure that if the truth of a privileged class of statements could be established, then the truth (or in some cases, the acceptability as hypotheses) of others could be guaranteed by a logic that is truth-preserving. Some sort of correspondence idea of truth guided the choice of the privileged class of propositions considered true in a primary sense. Thus, each of the candidates considered—axioms, empirical generalizations, observation reports, and ontic commitments implicit in the system as used—was defended as primary on the grounds that this was the most basic level in relating the system to the reality it explained.

In the last lecture we began by considering the meaning of 'true' and concluded by stressing the importance of conceptual frameworks in conditioning the meaning of propositions accepted as true. In this lecture we would like to see if we could fuse these two concerns. At one level they fuse rather easily; at a deeper level the synthesis is much more problematic. They fuse almost effortlessly at the level of the operative meaning of 'true' as assertible or acceptable. *Within* a scientific system, it is the practicing scientist and the community of scientific inquirers who decide which propositions are accepted as true. On this level the practicing scientist seems to have no reluctance about accepting a vast, potentially infinite number of scientific propositions as true. If one wants a decision procedure for generating such an infinite set, simply get a copy of *The Handbook of Chemistry and Physics,* which now runs to a few thousand pages of highly condensed scientific conclusions, begin to form propositions concerning such things as the specific resistance of different metals as a function of temperature, the number of protons in different types of atoms, the coefficient of expansion of different types of solids in different states, etc., etc., and then apply these propositions to an indefinite number of samples.

But such propositions are answers to internal questions. For the most part, the problems that bother the philosophers—and I include reflective scientists under the label 'philosophers' —also concern *external* questions. That is, they involve an evaluation of the validity and significance of a system as well as the acceptability of statements within a system. A realist and an operationalist would both be willing to accept as true the propositions generated from the *Handbook.* But this acceptance does not settle their disagreement as to whether such affirmed propositions can be detached from a particular scientific system and still be accepted as a statement of what obtains in reality. Such metascientific questions as realism vs. operationalism, Platonism vs. nominalism, reductionism vs. emergentism, and others, depend on whether propositions that are perfectly acceptable *within* a system (the acceptability of classes, the irreducibility of man, the existence of theoretical entities) should be accepted as true in a larger sense.

In discussing truth-claims in ordinary language, *our* ordinary language, it was reasonable to begin with individual propositions and work toward framework features, for these features have already been assimilated by normal language-users. The real problem was to make these implicit features explicit. But this same mode of procedure could prove disastrous when analyzing the significance and acceptability of propositions which function as part of a different conceptual framework, whether a primitive culture or a scientific system. To analyze such propositions while prescinding from the distinctive features of the conceptual framework is effectively to answer the question: What would we intend were we to affirm such a proposition? The pertinent question is: What does such a proposition mean within the linguistic community in which it functions? We must, accordingly, begin with general framework features and work toward individual propositions.

I

CONCEPTUAL FRAMEWORKS IN SCIENCE

My treatment of scientific systems as conceptual frameworks will depart from generally accepted ways of developing and explaining science. Perhaps I should begin by indicating where and why I break with tradition. Pierre Duhem serves as a convenient point of departure in explaining a distinctive aspect of the philosophy of science in the twentieth century. At the end of the nineteenth century, the majority of working scientists tended to think that the model of physical reality given by Newtonian physics represented reality as it exists objectively. Duhem's studies in the history of science, as well as his own work in thermodynamics, convinced him that different, even mutually incompatible conceptualizations of reality could be read into the same mathematical theory. Accordingly, he distinguished two aspects of scientific theory: a representative part, the formal mathematical structure; and an explanatory part, the conceptualization of reality implicit in the theory. This latter aspect represented, he felt, a disguised metaphysics. As such, it is not really a part of physics and plays no real role in the functioning of a scientific theory. His own summary statement is: "A physical theory is not an explanation. It is a system of mathematical propositions, deduced from a small number of principles, which aim to represent as simply, as completely, and as exactly as possible a set of experimental laws."[1]

This was not the view of most of his contemporaries, who felt that the explanatory part of science, the conceptualization of reality it presents, was an indispensable part of scientific systems. Why should anyone want to separate this aspect and dispense with it, since it was obviously true? With the overthrow of Newtonianism, these scientists had to abandon the simple and direct realism which served as a basis for interpreting the significance of scientific systems. With the rise of logical atomism and the eventual dominance of logical positivism in the philosophy of science, philosophers came more and more to focus on the logical structures which could be extracted from or read into scientific systems. The conceptualization of reality implicit in a theory was often identified with visualizable models, especially by those who tried to reduce all knowledge to a basis in sensation; it was then dismissed on the grounds that Heisenberg's indeterminacy principle implied that no visualizable model could possibly be an accurate representation of an atomic system. This approach generated its own difficulties, some of which were considered when mentioning "bottom of the page" interpretations of scientific systems. Recent reactions against such limitations tend to go to one of two extremes. One is to couple an even greater emphasis on logical analysis with an epistemology that breaks with the naive empiricism characteristic of logical positivism. In such an approach, the conceptualization of physical reality implicit in established theories is almost systematically disregarded, since the focus of attention is on the logical form thought to be proper to a rational reconstruction of scientific theories rather than on an analysis of actual theories. The other extreme is an historicism which analyzes the conceptual evolution that conditioned the actual development of scientific thought. Here, the conceptualization of reality implicit in scientific theories is clearly brought out, especially in discussing conceptual revolutions. But this has generally been done in such a descriptive way that logical and analytical tools necessary to treat the metascientific questions mentioned earlier were not the basis of the analysis.

It is interesting to note that the founders of the presently accepted interpretation of quantum mechanics, Neils Bohr and Werner Heisenberg, did try to analyze both the conceptual and logical problems involved in interpreting quantum theory. Philosophers of science have generally dismissed their epistemological ideas as naive, an opinion which I do not share. There was one philosopher of science, N. R. Hanson, who was trying to develop these diverse approaches simultaneously. In private discussions he admitted that he had not yet worked out an adequate way of interrelating an historical analysis of scientific development and a critical analysis of scientific systems. But he was convinced that this must be done. He was also convinced that those who dismissed the Copenhagen interpretation of quantum mechanics as epistemologically naive missed the real significance of what Bohr and Heisenberg had accomplished. Hanson's tragic death prevented him from accomplishing the synthesis he desired. Though the ideas to be presented are mine rather than his, many of them were either developed or sharpened through the sustained dialogue I had with him on these points during the two years we were together at Yale. Accordingly, I would like to think of what I am presenting here as something of a continuation of his work.

In the first lecture we considered two-component interpretations of scientific theories. I believe that this general idea is correct, but that both components have been systematically misinterpreted. One component was an observation language, but what was said about such a language was conditioned more by the requirements set by an empiricist theory of knowledge than by an analysis of the way language functions in science. The other component, the theoretical language, also tends to be predetermined by philosophical presuppositions, the key one being the assumption that any scientific theory can be rigorously redeveloped in the type of purely extensional formal system supplied by modern logic. As I attempted to show elsewhere, this can lead not only to a disregard of actual science but also to an uncritical projection of interpretative assumptions that are independent of, and often incompatible with, those actually operative in the interpretation of scientific theories.[2]

The two components I will discuss will be called 'a physical language' and 'a mathematical language' and symbolized by PL and ML. By a 'physical language' I mean essentially a transformed extension of ordinary language. The justification for stressing this comes from two considerations. First, any real language, any language that can be used to refer, describe, narrate, and explain, necessarily contains some conceptualization of reality, a point that was sufficiently belabored in the last lecture. Secondly, studies in the development of scientific thought by Hanson,[3] Kuhn,[4] Jaki,[5] Toulmin,[6] and others have shown the decisive importance any change in the conceptualization of reality plays in the advancement of science, a conceptualization that is embedded in and transmitted through the language used in scientific treatises. However, none of these authors have, in my opinion, given an adequate analysis of the epistemological problems involved in analyzing and explaining a conceptual revolution.

Elsewhere, I have attempted to present my ideas on the interpretation of scientific systems in a more technical form.[7] Here, I will try to present the same basic ideas in a non-technical way by means of plausibility arguments, an analogy, and selected use of historical examples. The analogy presupposes that you know how to play bridge, a reasonable presupposition with such a sophisticated audience.

We could explain the game of bridge by introducing two languages which we shall call the "game language" (GL) and the "strategy language" (SL). GL presupposes ordinary language (OL) and is essentially a specialized extension of OL containing the category terms required for unambiguous verbal specification of each card. In GL one states the *rules* for bridge and states the *facts* of particular hands.

There are various strategy languages, such as those advanced by Goren, Culbertson, and the Italian Blue Team. These are formal theoretical systems which can easily be reduced to axiomatic form. They are correlated with GL by means of correspondence rules. Thus, in the Goren SL, an ace corresponds to four points, a king to three, etc. The syntax of SL (or of a logical reconstruction of SL along axiomatic lines) would be basically that proper to a specification of arithmetic in logical terms supplemented by some further rules. These rules, unlike those in GL, are not a part of the game of bridge. One who opens with nine points may be playing bridge badly, but he is playing bridge. One who throws four cards in the kitty and opens with nine cards is not playing bridge badly—he is not playing bridge at all.

How does each of these languages relate to the reality in question, i.e., the thirteen cards in each of the four hands? In GL it is possible to affirm statements that are either true or false depending on whether or not they correspond to the facts: e.g., "My partner has the ace of spades." This, in fact, is the type of statement that warms the heart of the traditional epistemologist, a factual claim that can be verified by direct observation. But in bridge such direct observation of cards in other hands is called cheating—and it spoils our analogy. So let us first consider how we would evaluate the truth of such claims without cheating.

Consider a bidding sequence. I open with one spade and my partner replies one no trump. I go to two clubs and he answers two diamonds. When I bid two spades he jumps to three no trump and then I pass. On the basis of this bidding I conclude: (B_1) "My partner has at least one high heart and a couple of small ones"; (B_2) "My partner has about nine points." Then, in a reflective moment, I begin to wonder: What is the significance of asserting B_1 and B_2? B_1 in GL seems rather unproblematic. It is true if my partner has the K, 6, 3 of hearts or some similar combination, i.e., if what it states obtains in reality. B_2 seems a bit more problematic. Being a clever philosopher, I try to handle this by sheer analysis, employing techniques I have learned from philosophers of science. The analysis would run along something like the following lines.

Point counts are numbers and numbers are only intelligible as part of a mathematical system. They could, in fact, be called the ontic commitments of arithmetic. It follows that my partner does not have any points, because points are not the sort of things persons can possess. The semantic categorizations are incompatible. What he actually has are thirteen cards distributed into four suits. B_2 may be a reasonable inference within SL, but SL is ultimately just an inference mechanism. It only refers to reality through the mediation of correspondence rules. The forms it imposes are necessarily different from those proper to things in themselves. B_2 can only be given an operational interpretation and cannot be considered true in a correspondence sense.

After I finish this subtle analysis I lay down my hand, since I am dummy, and walk around the table to look at my partner's hand. One glance, coupled to a bit of counting, is sufficient to show that he does, in fact, have nine points—and makes me wonder about the appropriateness of my being called dummy. I feel the way Berkeley might have felt, had he watched Dr. Johnson kicking the stone.

GL is used primarily to describe and report. We tend to think of languages used for this purpose as transparent media, because they embody our understanding of the objects referred to. But both GL and SL relate to reality by means of formal conceptual systems containing category terms used to refer to objects. Since the category terms proper to GL (the names of the four suits and the thirteen different cards in each suit) not only provide a unique specification for each individual in the domain, but also furnish these individuals with names, while SL does not provide such a unique specification (four points means 1 ace, 2 queens, or 4 jacks) and is interpreted through correspondence rules, the two languages might seem to have radically different roles with regard to truth-claims. Here, however, the difference is more one of degree than of kind. One could develop a Goren type SL which could perform the roles played by *both* GL and SL.[8] If this new (and rather impractical) language came to be accepted as basic (e.g., in printing playing cards), then GL would have to be related to our new bridge language by means of correspondence rules. Correspondence rules, in short, link one language system to another language system. Which one is basic in referring to objects is ultimately a matter of choice, though in some situations only one choice is reasonable.

Now let us return to science considered as a two component system involving a physical language (PL) and a mathematical language (ML). To see how these relate to each other and to the reality to which they may be applied, let us begin with a simple example: mensuration. The basis for handling this in PL was clarified in the previous lecture in terms of descriptive metaphysics. Extension is spoken of as a property of bodies. By introducing predicates of predicates we may discuss the properties of length in terms of behavior under different operations. For length there are two basic joining operations to which all others may be reduced. One may juxtapose lengths in a straight line or join them perpendicularly. Using "+" as a symbol for linear joining, "×" as a symbol for rectilinear joining, and "o" to cover either operation, we may discuss the properties of length with respect to these operations.

First, either operation is *associative*. Thus, in a linear juxtaposition of three sticks the overall length is the same regardless of whether we first join a and b and then add c or first join b and c and then add a. The same indifference holds with respect to the resultant volume of a box if we first join length and width and then add height, or width and height and then add length. In symbols we should have the formula:

(1) $(a \mathbin{o} b) \mathbin{o} c = a \mathbin{o} (b \mathbin{o} c)$.

Similarly, the length is *commutative* under either joining. The net length is the same whether *a* is first and *b* second or vice versa, and the resultant area from rectilinear joining is the same whether *a* is the length and *b* the width or vice versa. In symbols:

(2) (a o b) = (b o a).

The third law, the *distributive* law, is a bit more complicated, since it combines linear and rectilinear joining. Think of two adjacent squares on a checkerboard and what is involved in measuring the total area of the two. One could either determine the area of each square by the "length times width" rule and then add the two areas together, or add the two linearly juxtaposed lengths together and multiply by their shared width. The result of the two methods would have to be the same. In symbols:

(3) a × (b + c) = (a × b) + (a × c).

Formulas (1), (2), and (3) also specify the properties of real numbers if "a," "b," and "c" represent numbers, "+" represents addition, and "×" multiplication, and "o" either operation. This gives a rather complex isomorphism between statements about properties of bodies in PL and statements about numbers in ML. The correspondence this entails can best be seen in a diagram.

PL		ML
Properties of properties	⟺	Properties of mathematical
with respect to		entities with respect to
Physical operations on	⟺	Mathematical operations on
Properties of	⟺	Mathematical entities
physical bodies		

First, a point on terminology. When I speak of properties rather than predicates, it is more a matter of convenience than of metaphysics. In Carnap's terms, I am using a material rather than a formal language. In PL the order of conceptualization is from the bottom up. That is, I think of a body with properties, though no aspect of the body is considered apart from being the bearer of the properties specified by the pertinent first-order predicates. If we wish to set up a mathematical system for treating these properties and their interrelations, then we must first find mathematical entities which stand for the properties in question. I use a single arrow to indicate this correspondence of mathematical entities standing for properties. The term 'mathematical entity' should not be taken as implying Platonic realism. It simply indicates that I can name a type of mathematical element, for example, real numbers, complex numbers, vectors, tensors, etc., which could be related to a definite property or relation by means of correspondence rules. The real question is: Which entities stand for which properties and under what conditions?

In the example given, real numbers (plus dimensions) stand for extension of one, two, or three dimensions. The basis of this correspondence is a set of two interrelated isomorphisms. First, there is an isomorphism (a one-one correspondence indicated by a double arrow) between physical operations which relate bodies by virtue of their extension (the two types of joining) and mathematical operations which relate numbers (addition and multiplication). Secondly, the properties of extension with respect to these physical operations are isomorphic to the properties of the mathematical entities defined with respect to the corresponding mathematical operations. Thus one set of formulas — (1), (2), and (3), plus two interpretations of the symbols —covers both cases.

These are the theory-dependent conditions of correspondence. There are also context-dependent conditions of correspondence. This is basically the requirement that the aspects of the physical situation that are not considered in the mathematical formulation do not play a role in the experimental situation. Thus, numbers are invariants and can only correspond to lengths if lengths are invariants. If the physical bodies in question were rubber bands whose lengths were not invariant in the experimental situation, the correspondence would not hold.

This simple example is sufficient to illustrate, but not to establish, the operative correspondence between PL and ML. A more detailed treatment gets rather technical and will be given elsewhere.[9] To keep the present treatment informal, I would like to consider the psychology involved rather than the logic. I am not trying to base an interpretation of science on a theory of psychology. My basis is still analytic, with the idea that there is a conceptualization of physical reality implicit in the language we use. But it might seem that the way I am developing this, in terms of two language systems and complex correspondence rules, does not fit the way we ordinarily know and speak about bodies, their properties, relations and operations. Such an objection could be fatal to my development, since I am trying to make explicit what is implicit in the ordinary practice of physics and have been arguing that one component of physics is an extension of ordinary language. What must be made plausible is the idea that we do know physical objects and their properties through the systematic utilization of conceptual systems having the type of formal properties indicated here.

The analytic aspect of this was treated in the last lecture, where we showed that the meaningfulness of predicates designating properties depends on the way these terms function as part of a conceptual system. What was not clarified was the role that properties of properties, defined with respect to definite physical operations, play in our ordinary knowledge. Is it a question of first knowing properties and then learning what a system has to say about them, or are these systematic features a normal, though not necessarily explicit, part of our ordinary knowledge?

Jean Piaget, the Swiss psychologist, and his co-workers have made a sustained investigation of this and related topics.[10] A basic problem Piaget considered was how a growing child comes to assimilate a physical property, i.e., represent it as a part of a cognitional schema. One of his simple but classical experiments involves having a child watch while the experimenter fills a tall thin glass with water, pours the water into a normal size glass and then into a short wide glass. In each case the water fills the glass to the brim. The question is then asked: "Which glass holds more water?" The child of four or five will usually pick out the tall glass, because it is higher. Here, as elsewhere, he focuses on one striking characteristic and is not capable of handling the simultaneous interrelation of two features, height and width. Without this cognitional capability, he cannot assimilate the idea that quantity is invariant under transformations of shape.

The growing child gradually assimilates this more complex idea. He does it first in an imaginative-intuitive way: if I squash the tall glass, the sides will bulge out and it will look like the other one. Eventually, he comes to understand this in terms of the principle involved: the volume of a fluid is independent of the shape of the container. He is incapable of explicitating this principle on his own. But suitable questions, such as those Socrates asked the slave boy in the *Meno*, would bring out the fact that this is the basis of his judgment.

By extending this type of experimental reasoning to other cases, Piaget and Inhelder have shown that a child has not adequately assimilated a property until he has also assimilated, though not necessarily explicitated, the properties this property has with respect to definite operations, e.g., invariance under transformation. This process of assimilation occurs at a stage of intellectual development (concrete operations) at which the view of reality implicit in the language the child speaks is gradually assuming an intellectual dominance over the prelinguistic sensory motor schemata that dominated the child's early years. Our ordinary knowledge of physical reality, accordingly, already involves a systematic interrelation of higher order properties specifying the properties that first-order properties and relations have with respect to specifiable physical transformations.[11]

The way PL and ML relate to each other and to the physical reality they somehow represent is similar to the way GL and

SL relate to each other and to a world of bridge hands. PL, an extension of OL, is used to categorize, to refer, and to describe, while ML, with its formal structure, is the vehicle for inference. This may seem to indicate that the way the two languages relate to reality is radically different. PL relates directly in that it represents physical reality, while ML only relates indirectly through the mediation of correspondence rules. While this is correct in a way, it can easily be given a misleading significance. Both PL and ML involve conceptual structure which can serve as vehicles for statements about physical reality. But PL (as an extension of OL) specifies what are objects, properties, and relations for us. In this sense it is object-centered while ML is essentially rule-centered. Yet, both can be used to make statements about physical objects which are reasonably accepted as true. Because PL supplies our normal means of specifying and referring to objects, ML statements which are *about* physical objects generally couple an ML predicate to a PL subject. The problems this involves will be treated when we consider different types of scientific propositions. But first it would be wise to flesh out the schematic account by some historical example selected to bring out the significance of PL as a revised extension of OL and some implications of the way it relates to ML.

II

CONCEPTUAL EVOLUTION AND REVOLUTION

The problem I wish to begin with is the problem discussed briefly in the first lecture: motion. The Aristotelian explanation of violent (as opposed to natural) motion was replaced in late medieval times by a theory of *impetus* (which held that the moving force was transmitted from the mover to the projectile rather than the medium). Galileo inherited these late medieval views and attempted to reduce them to an acceptable mathematical form. When this proved unsuccessful, he abandoned the causal notion of *impetus* and introduced *inertia,* a non-causal notion. We now think of inertia in terms of Newton's first law, the tendency of a body at rest to remain at rest or, if in motion, to remain in motion in a straight line unless acted upon by an external force. But there was a protracted period of conceptual confusion and gradual clarification before scientists could properly distinguish and adequately interrelate such key notions as inertia, momentum, and kinetic energy and relate them to such background notions as mass, extension, velocity, and acceleration.

Descartes was the first to attempt this through a rigorously developed, consistent conceptualization of material reality. In his view, physical bodies were essentially characterized by extension, so that any further properties attributable to bodies should be reducible to extension. He explained inertia, accordingly, as the product of a body's extension and speed. The mathematical theory of collisions he worked out on this basis was a notorious failure.

Newton considered mass, rather than extension, the basic property of bodies, defined momentum as the product of mass and velocity (speed plus direction), and used these notions to develop the theory of mechanics that marked the beginning of modern science and was a decisive turning point in the intellectual history of the Western world. From the work of Newton and his followers came the conceptualization of physical reality which dominated Western thought for three hundred years, and which is still quite influential. The main outlines of this view are familiar by now. Space and time are absolutes. Physical bodies can be thought of as collections of material particles endowed with such primary qualities as mass, inertia, and gravitational attraction. Secondary qualities, such as color, taste, etc., should, in principle, be explained by reduction to primary qualities. Extension has a somewhat ambiguous status in the Newtonian schema. The extension of the postulated elementary particles played no role in the physical theory, while the extension of larger bodies might be explained either through an addition of elementary extensions or through the space separating these elementary particles, an idea that was later developed in detail by Boscovitch.[12]

The physical language used in Newtonian mechanics was a transformed extension of ordinary language. Neils Bohr and Werner Heisenberg repeatedly pointed this out in contrasting classical physics with quantum mechanics.[13] Their contention that classical physics represents an extension of ordinary language has, to my knowledge, never been accepted by any philosopher in the analytic tradition—apart from myself. The reasons are obvious. Mathematical physics is quite a different thing from ordinary language. This is especially obvious when one's judgment is based on what philosophers say science should be, rather than on what physicists say science is.

What was less than obvious was that, until recently, analytic philosophy had not supplied the tools requisite to clarify what Bohr had said. And it must be admitted that some of his expressions badly require clarification. The real point at issue is not the syntactic structures or the varying uses to which the language is put, but the descriptive metaphysics, the conceptualization of reality, implicit in the language used. Or, in the language of the Copenhagen interpretation, the terms 'particle' and 'wave' as used in classical physics presuppose the ordinary language notion of 'substance,' and it was this notion that quantum mechanics modified.

In principle it is possible to have various types of ontologies undergirding the language used in a scientific theory. One could have an ontology in which events are basic and objects, conceived as concrescences of events, have a derivative status. Whitehead developed such a view in detail. One could have an ontology in which bare particulars, sense-data, an all-pervading Spinozistic substance, or fields are basic with particles as singularities in fields.[14] But the descriptive metaphysics of classical physics is fundamentally that proper to Indo-European languages. Reality is conceived of as an interrelated collection of things with properties moving in a space-time continuum.

Aristotle, the first and one of the greatest analytic philosophers, brought out one aspect of this descriptive metaphysics that is significant in the present context. His famous categories (substance, quantity, quality, etc.) reflect a conceptual ordering proper to ordinary language. Thus, quality inheres in substance through the mediation of quantity or, in Locke's terms, secondary qualities inhere in substance through the mediation of primary qualities. Thus, it is a conceptual *a priori* of OL that whatever is colored is extended, while the reverse is not the case, because a body's being colored depends on its being extended. It is because of this hierarchical ordering of categories that the type of conceptual relocation of secondary qualities proper to the Newtonian physical language leaves the underlying conceptual schema essentially intact. With familiar qualities gone, the criteria which serve to distinguish different natures, in Aristotle's sense of "nature," are also gone. All bodies are conceived of as extended collections of material particles having mass, inertia, and gravitational attraction. These are the individuals which serve as the basic particulars of the new conceptual framework. Like the basic particulars of OL, they are conceived of as things with properties moving in a space-time continuum. In this sense the PL of Newtonian physics is a transformed extension of OL.[15]

The relation between this conceptualization of reality and a mathematical formalism is complicated by the fact that the type of geometric formulation Newton used was not followed by later physicists. Rather than attempt to untangle these complexities, I will give one illustrative example and then move on to a different case which gives a better insight into the significance of the relation between PL and ML. The example is Newton's treatment of gravity. One of the key features in working out the consequences of Newton's postulate that gravity obeyed an inverse square law was the proof that the gravitational attraction of a spherically symmetrical body acted as if all the mass were concentrated in the center. Newton did this in two stages. The first stage was almost pure mathematics. He considered bodies which were just collections of mass particles (he called them "corpuscles") and hence could be broken down into shells and strips without changing the bodies in any significant way. For such bodies he worked out a set of theorems concerning an inverse square centripetal force.[16] For the second stage, after all the mathematics was worked out, he identified these spherically symmetric bodies with the planets and centripetal force with gravity. What this and similar examples illustrate is that, though Newton and most of his followers did not think of complex bodies (especially living ones) as nothing but aggregates of mass particles, whatever further qualifications they had did not function as part of the machinery of Newtonian mechanics.

The more revealing example for the interrelation of PL and ML is the development of thermodynamics. At the end of the eighteenth century, Farenheit and Celsius developed temperature scales, a basis for applying numbers to degrees of heat. The attempt to develop a mathematical science on this simple basis failed because temperature is not an additive property under the operation of mixing bodies of different temperatures. Joseph Black supplied the key concepts needed: a distinction between degrees of temperature and quantity of heat, a distinction between overt and latent heat, and the notion of a specific heat characterizing different substances. At this time heat was thought of as a fluid with both chemical and thermal properties. The conceptualization became clearer after Lavoisier rejected the phlogiston theory of combustion and, in his monumental *Traité Élémentaire de Chemie* (1889), listed caloric as a basic element.

Caloric was thought of as an indestructible, uncreatable weightless elastic fluid whose particles repel one another (which explains the diffusion of heat), and are attracted by particles of ordinary matter, the magnitude of the attraction being different for different substances and different states of the same substance. This model served as a basis for a mathematical theory of heat which was quite successful. Since the quantity of heat is a measure of the caloric present, and caloric is uncreatable and indestructible, heat is a conserved quantity and can be characterized by real numbers obeying additive laws.

Though this mathematics was correct in its treatment of heat exchange and related phenomena, the conceptualization of heat as caloric was incorrect, something Count Rumford established. The problem then was to develop a new conceptualization of heat which would preserve the valid mathematical laws established on the basis of the caloric theory. Joule, Mayer, Kelvin, Maxwell, and others did this by establishing the idea that heat is a form of energy, that energy is conserved, and that it exists in latent (or potential) as well as overt forms. The first-order predicates, those that embody a conceptualization of what heat is, changed. But they changed in such a way as to preserve the second-order predicates that ground the correspondence with a mathematical formalism. The applicability of numbers to characterize the quantity of heat in a system requires a conservation law for heat, and this, in turn, requires the notion of specific heats and latent heats.

The conceptualization of the phenomenon in question, characterized by a set of first-order predicates, changed from "Heat is a manifestation of caloric" to "Heat is a form of energy." But the established mathematical formalism perdured. The reason for this is the fact that the new and the old conceptualizations share a set of second-order predicates, predicates whose primary function is to express laws of conservation and invariance under certain transformations, or, as Wigner has characterized them, laws about the laws of nature.[17] Numbers can stand for quantities of heat, provided numbers and quantities of heat share formally similar properties under corresponding operations. If joining bodies of differing temperatures together in an isothermal container (with heat considered as a property of the body that contains it) is the physical operation corresponding to addition in mathematics, then heat is associative and commutative under this operation.

To complete this view of science as involving a set of conceptualizations of reality, we need one further example. We have already considered a key example illustrating the conceptualization of reality implicit in classical (i.e., pre-1925) physics and the way in which it represents a transformed extension of ordinary language. The example of thermodynamics was intended to bring out how a two-component interpretation of science allows both for conceptual revolutions and for an underlying continuity. What we must now consider is the greatest conceptual revolution in modern physics, the development of quantum mechanics. What I would like to do is to give a nontechnical summary of ideas that will be developed more technically elsewhere. Since I believe that the philosophy of science should explain the science of the scientists rather than the idealized logical systems that the philosophers themselves construct, I will focus on the formulation of quantum mechanics that synthesized the wave mechanics of Schrödinger and the matrix mechanics of Heisenberg and also supplied the basic framework for further developments. This is the formulation of quantum mechanics given by P. A. M. Dirac.

At the beginning of his book, Dirac stated the type of scientific formulation he was developing:

The new schema becomes a precise physical theory when all the axioms and rules governing the mathematical quantities are specified and when in addition certain laws are laid down connecting physical facts with the mathematical formalism, so that from any given physical conditions equations between the mathematical quantities may be inferred and vice versa.[18]

This statement of Dirac actually supplied the basis for the terminology we have been using in our two-component interpretations of scientific theories. The heart of this interpretation is an explicitation of the logical structure implicit in Dirac's quantum mechanics. Accordingly, the fact that his quantum mechanics fits beautifully into my interpretative framework should come as no surprise. All that I have to do now is to indicate how his PL and ML are developed and interrelated.

His physical system is based on established facts and reasonable assumptions. The facts are of two kinds. He assumes the existence of definite specifiable physical systems, e.g., electrons, hydrogen atoms, etc. Secondly, it is assumed that some properties characterizing these systems, such as mass, energy, electrical charge and angular momentum, can be specified. The latter point, however, has some restrictions peculiar to quantum mechanics. Calling 'the state of a system' the maximum number of characterizing physical properties that can be simultaneously specified, Dirac assumes, on the basis of experimental evidence, that the state of an atomic system cannot be completely specified in classical terms.

The novel, non-classical idea introduced is the superposition principle. The state of an atomic system can be considered a superposition of two or more distinct states. That this is incompatible with classical conceptualizations of matter shared by OL and classical physics is easily seen by trying to apply this principle to a classical case. Imagine a man weighing 175 pounds being weighed on scales that only record weights of either 150 or 200 pounds. If the superposition principle applied, the original man could be considered a superposition of two men, one weighing 150 and one weighing 200 pounds. Any given weighing would select one of the two superimposed men. A sufficient number of such weighings would average 175. The difficulty here is not just that a weighing, the measurement of a classical property, *does* not produce such results, but that it *cannot* without involving a contradiction in the conceptualization involved. Men just do not come that way.

But photons do. Prepare a photon with a polarization in a certain direction. Then set up a polarization analyzer which will only pass photons whose polarization is 45° away from the direction in which the photons were polarized. A certain precisely specifiable percentage of the photons get through. Polarization in a given direction, accordingly, can be considered a superposition of two (or more) polarizations in directions on either side of the original.

The state of a system is the specification of all its properties.

If mathematical entities are to represent states, then these mathematical entities must have the same properties that states have. They must obey a superposition principle. Because vectors (mathematical entities that have both magnitude and direction) have this property, Dirac chose vectors to represent states of systems. Since the vectors are complex quantities in a space with an infinite number of mutually perpendicular directions, we will not say any more about his mathematics. The only point we need is that it does fit the interpretative framework we have developed. Mathematical entities represent properties of physical systems because the first-order properties of the mathematical entities correspond to second-order properties of physical systems, i.e., properties of properties defined with respect to some operation.

In quantum theory, accordingly, one still uses the language of things with properties moving in a space-time framework. This much of the OL descriptive metaphysics carries over. But the way these properties are conceptualized represents a further and more drastic break with OL. In the descriptive metaphysics of OL, primary and secondary qualities are both real objective determinations of bodies. In classical physics only primary qualities, extensive magnitudes that can be represented by numbers, are considered real. Secondary qualities play a role in the formal system only if they can be defined in terms of, or explained by reduction to, primary qualities. But primary qualities are still spoken of as objectively real determinations of physical bodies.

The descriptive metaphysics implicit in the language of quantum mechanics differs from this descriptive metaphysics shared by OL and classical physics in two basic respects. First, one cannot apply this language to actual observations, e.g., in referring, recording, or describing, without explicitly determining for each case the line separating the subject from the objective system. This determination is effectively accomplished by the way a particular experiment is set up. Secondly, the attribution of measurable properties to a body is, in general, context-dependent. This means that they cannot be thought of as objective determinations of beings the way they were in classical physics. This applies to any properties covered by the superposition principle.[19]

In summary, the way science relates to reality is basically an extension of the way ordinary language relates to reality: through people using language to refer, describe, narrate, and explain. This transformed extension of ordinary language is something we have dubbed a 'physical language.' It cannot fulfill its role unless it implicitly contains a conceptualization of the domain of reality to which it is applied.

This physical language is correlated with a mathematical formalism. The basis of the correlation is generally (it varies slightly with different systems) a correspondence between properties of physical objects. specified by the physical language, and mathematical entities, e.g., numbers, vectors, tensors, etc. The conditions for the correspondence are rather complex. First, there must be an isomorphism between a mathematical operation on the mathematical entities employed (e.g., adding numbers, rotating vectors) and a physical operation operating on the properties correlated with these entities (e.g., linear juxtaposition of lengths, changing a property—technically a dynamic variable—of an atomic system). Secondly, the properties of the physical property defined with respect to this physical operation, must be isomorphic to the properties of the mathematical entity defined with respect to the corresponding mathematical operation. If these conditions are fulfilled, then mathematical entities represent specifiable physical properties. One may then specify a physical system in PL, use the correspondence with ML to set up the appropriate equations, solve these equations, and then use the same correspondence rules in reverse to give a physical significance (in PL) to the conclusions (derived in ML).

Both PL and ML involve conceptual structures. The basic differences between them are: first, that ML is structured by formal explicit rules, while in PL the rules are informal, usually tacit, and the conceptualization of objects is dominant; second-ly, there is a difference in use. Because PL is an extension of OL and implicitly contains a conceptualization of the reality treated, PL is used to refer and describe, while ML is related to physical reality by rules connecting it with PL.

One establishes such a connection so that the precise and powerful inferential mechanisms developed in mathematics may be of service in physical reasoning. In the historical de-velopment of physics, such mathematical formalisms have come to play a more and more dominant role while the physical language tends toward the functional minimum necessary to interpret the mathematical formalism. But a minimum there must be, and this minimum necessarily embodies a conceptual-ization of the reality being considered. In other sciences, e.g., biology, where description and qualitative reasoning are more important, the role of a physical conceptualization is larger while that of a mathematical formalism is smaller. With this gradual clarification we may now consider the problem of the significance of labeling various types of scientific propositions 'true.'

III

TRUTH CLAIMS IN SCIENTIFIC SYSTEMS

Labeling a proposition 'true' is equivalent to asserting it. The working scientist has little difficulty either in asserting propositions in his discipline or in separating true ones from false or doubtful ones. It is true that metals conduct electricity, that the hydrogen atom has one proton, that ordinary table salt is a crystalline compound of sodium and chlorine. The number of scientific claims that can be reasonably affirmed is virtually unlimited.

Yet, it is the very facility with which the scientist can make such claims that raises the problem of truth on a more funda-mental level. The intent of a truth-claim is to state what is the case in reality. The scientist, particularly the reflective scientist, is aware that his technical statements are formulated within a conceptual framework that is a product of an historical development, that it represents a simplified idealization of a certain domain of reality, that it is subject to change, even revolutionary change, and that it is in need of interpretation. Such reflections on the scientific enterprise inevitably make one wonder about the degree to which statements reasonably accepted as true describe the really real.

Before attempting to answer such a question it is necessary to specify it a bit more precisely. To do this we shall consider three classes of propositions found in scientific writings: factual claims, empirical generalizations, and theoretical statements. The basic question that concerns us in considering each of these types of propositions is: To what degree does accepting a proposition as true entail accepting as true the conceptualization of reality implicit in the system in which the proposition functions?

1. *Factual Claims*

By a 'factual claim' I mean essentially a singular statement purporting to report what is the case in reality for an individual or a class of individuals. In the cases of concern here, such claims will usually employ technical scientific terms. Thus: "A proton entered the bubble chamber at time t_0 and collided with a neutron at time t_1," "The meter reads six volts" and "The normal oxygen atom has 8 protons, 8 neutrons, and 8 electrons" would exemplify the sort of claim intended.

A couple of initial points should be noted. First, including statements about classes of individuals (e.g., all hydrogen atoms) as well as about particular individuals inevitably entails having a fuzzy border between factual claims and empirical generalizations. I have attempted to draw the line where it seems to be operative in scientific practice rather than follow *a priori* logical norms. Thus, the experimentalist attempting to report particular results would have to include in his calculations statements or data about particular individuals, the number of protons in a carbon atom, the specific conductivity of the silver wire used, etc. Such statements are generally obtained from handbooks on the assumption that what is true of one is true of all and vice versa.[20]

Secondly, the role I am attributing to factual claims is roughly comparable to the role positivists attributed to observation statements, but the epistemological underpinning is quite different. Factual claims are not, nor are they intended to be, a transcription into empiricist language of the given of immediate experience. They may involve a theoretical background and a process of reasoning: e.g., in interpreting the series of events depicted in a photograph of a bubble chamber.

In the second lecture we considered factual claims made within an ordinary language framework. There it was argued that the acceptance of such propositions as true entailed two further conclusions. First, in making such claims one is using —but not necessarily affirming—a conceptualization of reality, or a descriptive metaphysics. Roaring sky-gods, wrestling devils, and colors as formally present in objects were implicitly affirmed in sentences using these ontic commitments to make statements accepted as true. Even when, thanks to a different and more developed conceptualization of reality, these aspects of the conceptualization were dropped or denied, one could still accept the propositions in question as true. But the truth-claim in the latter instance is minimal. The proposition is accepted as true if interpreted as an observation report, but not as an ontological claim.

The second conclusion drawn was that from within a given conceptual system it is not possible to specify the precise degree to which one affirming a proposition must also affirm the presuppositions, framework features, and logical entailments which condition the meaningfulness of the proposition affirmed. These two conclusions suggest some definite limitations for a correspondence theory of truth. One affirming a factual proposition, "S is P," intends to state what is the case in reality. All that is strictly required for the proposition to be true is a functional correspondence. 'S' must fulfill its role as a referential expression; 'P' must be intelligible as a predicate attached to 'S' and predicated of the object to which 'S' refers. The average speaker certainly does not make statements with such functional and formal limitations in mind. He may think that 'S' specifies what an object is and that 'P' designates an objective determination of this object. Such tacit assumptions are quite reasonable and generally harmless provided the linguistic system is functioning adequately and unambiguously. But one is justified in formally asserting these assumptions only by explicitating the pertinent framework features and having a reflective grasp of evidence sufficient to warrant assent.

These general considerations apply to factual claims made within scientific systems. But the problem of truth is more clearly framework-dependent. In the vast majority of cases, the scientist can determine which factual claims are true, i.e., assertible. If he wonders what it really means to say that they are true, or whether they are true in an ultimate sense, he is effectively wondering about the manner in which and the degree to which the correspondence with reality intended in an asserted claim is fulfilled.

Here the bridge analogy, previously developed, may help to disentangle the complexity of facts and propositions. The strategy language of bridge, like the mathematical language employed in a physical theory, is intelligible but empty. Neither, of itself, gives any information about physical reality. Both are used by being coupled to two types of propositions. The first type are general background propositions that are accepted as true. Thus we have in GL such propositions as, "My partner has thirteen cards divided into four suits and cannot have any two cards with the same descriptive tag," or, in PL, "The normal aluminum atom has thirteen electrons divided into three energy levels and cannot have any two electrons with the same descriptive tag (i.e., set of four quantum numbers)." By building on such background presuppositions, one can introduce particular factual information and argue to particular conclusions by means of the inference language, whether SL or ML. Let us match the two bridge inferences, previously given, concerning my partner's heart honor and nine points with some physics inferences recently drawn by Murray Gell-Mann which you might have noted in the newspapers: (P_1) "The $\Omega-$ (omega minus particle) decays into a proton by a three step process"; (P_2) "The $\Omega-$ has a minus three strangeness quantum number." As with the bridge example, one might be tempted to argue that P_1 is a factual claim, since it describes what happens objectively, but that P_2 is different and only a factual claim in an indirect sense requiring interpretation. Since strangeness quantum numbers are only intelligible as part of a theoretical system, they are not the sort of thing particles can have.[21] P_2, accordingly, should be taken as an elliptical form of a complex of sentences involving factual claims, correspondence rules, and mathematical statements.

As with the earlier example of B_1 and B_2, the idea that P_1 and P_2 cannot both be considered factual claims hinges on the naive idea that factual claims represent a transcription into language of things as they are in themselves or, for a strict empiricist, of the given of immediate experience. But any attribution of properties to bodies depends on a conceptual system both in its manner of specifying and referring to entities and in the meaning of the predicates attributing properties to them. Factual claims, accordingly, are represented either by propositions in PL or by propositions joining a PL subject (used to refer) to an ML predicate (used to specify or attribute).

A factual claim using such scientific terms implicitly affirms that the terms used correspond to distinguishable properties or relations of the objects treated. It need not, however, affirm the background conceptualization. That is, it need not affirm the statements that would result from making the descriptive metaphysics explicit and affirming it as true. Here scientific usage is more precise than ordinary usage in distinguishing between what is and what is not affirmed.

Consider a concrete example: "The proton has unit charge and half-integral spin." The physicist accepts this as true in a rather unproblematic way. This proposition uses a category term, 'proton,' to report regularities. Implicit in the conceptualization employed is the functional assumption that the proton is a fundamental unit and that these are some of the properties characterizing it. It may well be that the proton is not an irreducible unit. It may be composed of more fundamental units such as quarks, or it may be a stable interaction of more fundamental fields. Such possibilities supply working hypotheses guiding current research. All that is required for the truth of this scientific proposition is that the term 'proton' can have a referential role and that whatever it refers to functions as a unit as far as this level of explanation is concerned.[22]

Is the doctrine I am presenting here realism or pure relativism? I think that this is too crude a dichotomy. Something a bit more subtle is needed. Rather than take realism as a full-blown philosophical theory—which goes beyond our considerations by presupposing a treatment of the critical problem—we will consider a minimal but indispensable claim for any doctrine of realism: factual claims are true or false by virtue of what obtains in reality and not merely by virtue of conventions concerning the proper use of words. The doctrine presented here is certainly realistic in this minimal sense.

There is an abiding temptation to read a strong correspondence view into factual claims made within science, a correspondence view that effectively projects into reality the framework features of our conceptual systems. The argument would run along the same lines familiar from common sense realism as, for example, in textbooks of Scholastic epistemology or in the writings of G. E. Moore. We can affirm factual claims as true and as known with certainty to be true. But such propositions would not be true unless reality is as we say it is. What such an analysis effectively does is to consider language when it is idling rather than when it is functioning.

An analysis of such affirmed propositions in their actual

functioning as part of a conceptual framework justifies a minimal, and not precisely specifiable, functional correspondence through the use of a conceptualization of reality and the roles of reference and predication. The fact that we can make statements about physical reality which are known with certainty to be true does not, of itself, imply that we know this reality in any ultimate sense. There is still room for advancement, an advancement that may entail drastic conceptual revolutions. The possibility of such advancement brings us to our second level: empirical generalizations.

2. *Empirical Generalizations*

By 'empirical generalizations' I mean general laws which are obtained—or are obtainable in principle—from an analysis of experimental data rather than derived as theorems within a theory. Some examples are the gas laws of Boyle, Charles, and Gay-Lussac, Kepler's laws of planetary motion, and the laws for spectral lines discovered by Balmer, Rydberg, and others. In his detailed treatment of such laws, Nagel defended the position that empirical generalizations differ from theories in that they are expressed in one law rather than by a collection of axioms and rules, they can be confirmed or refuted in a fairly direct sense, and they can precede the theories that are introduced to explain them and can survive their demise.[23] Though the borderlines separating such laws from factual statements at one end of the explanatory spectrum and theoretical statements at the other are rather fuzzy and their precise location somewhat arbitrary, there is a reasonable basis for this distinction. What we are concerned with here is the question of whether it is appropriate to predicate 'true' and 'false' of such empirical generalizations and what the implications of such predication are.

It would undoubtedly be possible to distinguish various types of empirical generalizations in any one science, and then multiply this by the number of sciences involved. For our present, rather limited, purposes we shall simply consider one division which has a distinct bearing on the problem of truth.

Empirical generalizations can be either descriptive-categorical or quantitative. By 'descriptive-categorical' I am referring to those generalizations concerned with putting objects into categories and then predicating properties or relations of them as members of a class. Thus Carl Linnaeus' great contribution to biology was his system of classification of animals and plants (his classifications of diseases, minerals, and men of science into military ranks with himself as general were less useful). Plants, for example, were grouped into classes, orders, genera, and species. The proper classification of a plant gives a considerable amount of information, e.g., about its method of reproduction.

The peculiar aspect of the problem of truth that concerns us with respect to this type of empirical generalization is the problem of linguistic conventions. To what degree are laws, based on such a descriptive-categorical framework, simply rules for the proper use of terms, or conceptual *a prioris* (for example, any object belonging to a species belongs to that species' genus), rather than empirical generalizations that are true or false by virtue of what obtains in reality? A particular case may serve to bring out the significance of this problem. When Lavoissier discovered oxygen, he identified it in terms of its gross properties: an odorless, colorless gas, which is the component of ordinary air supporting combustion and respiration.[24] After the development of atomic and nuclear physics, it was gradually discovered that all normal oxygen atoms contain eight protons and eight electrons. When it was realized that this was more basic than oxygen's microscopic properties, 'oxygen' was effectively redefined in terms of its atomic composition.

Consider now the proposition: "All oxygen atoms have eight protons," a proposition whose acceptability is not in question. Is this an empirical generalization—and thus true by virtue of the facts it reports—or is it really a definition—and thus true by virtue of the act of defining? One might be tempted to say that it was an empirical generalization but has become a defined truth. But it sounds rather strange to say that a factually true proposition has ceased to be factual while remaining true.

The actual situation becomes clearer if we return to the notion of systems and the idea of expanding and changing them, or having conceptual revolutions. The acceptance of atomic physics necessitated such a conceptual revolution in the chemistry of elements. In both pre- and post-revolutionary chemistry, it is a fact, established on empirical grounds, that a certain cluster of microscopic properties is associated with a certain atomic configuration. The way in which this is stated will involve definitions within each system (macroscopic and submicroscopic) and rules establishing correspondences between them. If, following the tradition of science, the system accepted as explanatory is considered basic, while the macroscopic system is considered relatively phenomenological, then it is reasonable to accept the atomic definitions as more basic.

In such a case we would say that the propositions in question are true by convention within a system, while the acceptance of the system is based, in large part, on empirical reasons. Both before and after the acceptance of a conceptual revolution, a general factual claim is expressed through a linguistic system, though the manner in which this is done undergoes internal changes. To the degree that the empirical generalization becomes accepted as a background assumption, it can be treated as the type of factual claim just considered.

This is hardly a novel idea. Aristotle insisted that the analysis on which explanation is based moves from what is clear to us to what is fundamental in reality. If one successfully completes such an analysis, then he pivots intellectually and uses the principles attained by analysis as the basis of explanation. Contemporary analysis, particularly Oxford analysis, has somewhat obscured this because of its concentration on explication rather than explanation. But the Aristotelian ideal is still viable. What is novel and non-Aristotelian in the present situation is the dialectical process of development through the replacement and reformulation of systems. This very pluralism of conceptual systems undercuts any simple argument from what is basic in particular systems or conceptual frameworks to what is basic in reality. In summary, it is possible to accept as true a vast number of classificatory and descriptive empirical generalizations. But this need not, of itself, entail accepting the conceptual system as true in a correspondence sense. What this implies, in particular, is that the fact that we can make statements which are true of all and only members of a class does not of itself imply that the class name denotes a natural species.

The dependence of empirical generalizations on conceptual frameworks can be specified a bit more precisely when we consider those generalizations that are fundamentally quantitative, e.g., Boyle's law, Kepler's law, etc. Such laws inevitably involve a simplification and an idealization of the matter treated. The gas laws apply strictly only to an ideal gas, while Kepler's laws fit planets moving around a central force only to the degree that one can prescind from the perturbing effect of other planets. The really interesting point here is the relative role of the two components considered earlier, the physical language and the mathematical language.

To clarify this we may return once again to the analogy developed long ago between GL and SL in bridge and PL and ML in science. One point of the analogy is to show the operative difference between truth-claims in a functioning language and legal definitions. One who says, either directly or through his bid, that he has at least thirteen points is certainly not telling the whole truth. Some guessing is still in order. Nor, from the point of view of the analyst as hedgehog, is he telling nothing but the truth.[25] Such an analyst could read into his statement misleading implications: for example, the idea that points are the sort of things people may possess. Nevertheless, he is telling the truth—or he better be if he wishes to continue playing bridge. Though statements about point counts are part of a formal system which requires interpretation, primarily because a formal system is not our usual basis for categorizing reality, nevertheless they are true or false by virtue of what obtains in reality.

Now let us consider some simple—simple in the sense that

my examples simplify the history in question—examples involving PL and ML. This is most easily done schematically.

System	Conceptualization of Gravity	Math. Formula
Galileo	Constant force field around the earth	$F = \text{const.}$
Newtonianism	Action at a distance	$F = GMm/r^2$
Einstein	Warping of space in the presence of massive objects	$R\mu\nu = O$
Quantized gravitation	Exchange of spin two gravitons	? ? ?

If we compare the statements in PL and ML, we notice a
radical difference between the two series. The statements in PL
present competing and mutually incompatible conceptualizations of the same basic phenomenon. If gravity is action at a
distance, it is independent of the properties of the intervening
space.[26] If it is a property of space, it is not an interchange of
particles. Yet the mathematical formulations exhibit a fundamental continuity in that each reduces to its predecessor in the
limits in which the predecessor is valid. Thus, Newton's law
yields a difference of about two parts in a hundred thousand
for the difference between the gravitational force at the top and
bottom of the tower of Pisa, a difference too small to be measured by any means available to Galileo.

In view of these complications, a simple correspondence
view of truth applied to empirical generalizations leads to
paradoxes. The PL propositions state what is the case (Gravity
is . . . ; heat is . . .) and would seem to be the *prima facie* contenders for the status of being true or false. But the PL propositions listed are mutually incompatible. If one is true, the others
must be false. If we accept the latest as the truest—as one generally does with fashions—then we would have to say that the
Galilean, Newtonian, and Einsteinian explanations of gravity
are false, while the yet to be constructed quantum theory may
be correct.

Such a position is obviously untenable, for it renders the normal functioning of science unintelligible. A way out of this difficulty which has an initial plausibility is the Duhemian one of dismissing the conceptualization of reality implicit in a scientific theory as excess baggage, a psychological crutch that is really not a part of physics. The real physics is the set of mathematical laws expressed in ML. I find this view untenable for the reasons discussed earlier. If the conceptualization of physical reality implicit in an empirical generalization is simply disregarded, while the mathematical form is retained, then there is no non-arbitrary way to give this mathematical formalism a physical interpretation.

The crucial task, accordingly, in treating the truth of empirical generalizations is to explain the precise role this conceptualization plays. In the two-component interpretation developed here, the correspondence between the conceptualization of physical reality embodied in PL and the mathematical formalism hinges on an isomorphism between propositions involving second-order physical predicates and propositions involving first-order mathematical predicates. The propositions involving first-order physical predicates embody the conceptualization of reality. They specify the properties, relations, and activities attributed to the objects proper to the framework. Second-order physical propositions, stating properties of properties, formulate such things as conservation laws and invariances under transformation. When physical frameworks undergo conceptual revolutions, the second-order propositions correlated with mathematical laws must manifest a basic continuity similar to that displayed by mathematical laws interpreted as successive approximations.

Thus, in thermodynamics the conservation of caloric becomes a restricted case of the conservation of energy. Successive theories of gravitation include energy conservation as a basic law, though they are at variance with regard to how potential energy is to be understood. Such considerations, I believe, supply a basis for considering the peculiar truth status of empirical generalizations. Accepting such an empirical generalization as true entails accepting the mathematical formulation as true of reality within specifiable limits. A proposition in ML or the type of mixed PL-ML propositions discussed earlier may be true of physical reality in the same way that a proposition in SL may be true of a bridge hand. Such a proposition requires interpretation, but differing PL's may supply the category terms and the conceptualization requisite for interpretation. Accordingly, accepting an empirical generalization as true entails accepting the idea that its formulation in PL is *covariant* with respect to conceptual transformations.

Since this idea is somewhat novel, a brief elaboration might help. The term 'covariant' is borrowed from the special theory of relativity. The two basic postulates of this theory are the *invariance* of the speed of light in a vacuum and the *covariance* of the laws of physics under inertial transformations. That is, when a law is changed from one set of coordinates to another, the components of the law change; they are not invariant. But they change in such a way that the overall form remains the same. In contemporary physics, this is usually accomplished automatically by the use of a special notation.[27]

Empirical generalizations usually straddle different conceptualizations of the same domain. This is partially because of the type of historical development through conceptual revolutions just discussed, and partially because of the difference between the observational framework in which the empirical generalization is formulated and the theoretical framework in which it may—in some sense—be explained. Thus the gas laws relate: temperature and pressure of a gas, if one is considering the empirical generalization which was historically developed on inductive grounds; *or* average kinetic energy and momentum transfer of molecules, if one is considering the theoretical counterpart of this empirical generalization.

Accepting an empirical generalization as true need not entail accepting the conceptualization employed as correct or irreformable. What it does entail is that any subsequent conceptualization of the same domain contains propositions which play the role played by empirical generalizations accepted as true in the original framework. The particular framework specifies the type of entities discussed, e.g., gas or molecules in motion, and the properties and relations attributed to these entities. What is *invariant* is the expression of the properties these properties have with respect to definite operations. This means that the metalinguistic form of an empirical generalization (or laws about the laws of nature) is invariant, while the empirical generalization itself, if true, is *covariant*.

As with the invariance discussed in high energy physics, once they are clarified they may be softened by being called approximate rather than strict invariants. The significance of this may be seen by returning to our interpretative base. This was the correspondence between properties of physical properties defined with respect to some physical operation and properties of mathematical entities defined with respect to a corresponding mathematical operation. This gives an isomorphism between propositions in PL and ML. If successive mathematical formulations represent more accurate approximations, then the corresponding empirical generalizations cannot be strictly covariant.

It was possible to elaborate the idea that affirming an empirical generalization as true implies affirming an essential covariance with respect to conceptual transformations because of the role of mathematical formulations in supplying a basis for continuity across such transformations. But now, like the stage magician who yanks the tablecloth from under the dishes, we can pull out the role of mathematics without shattering the general conclusion. Even for the type of categorical-descriptive empirical generalizations previously considered, affirming them as true entails affirming an essential covariance with respect to conceptual transformations. This, in fact, is the basic criterion distinguishing general statements which are true because they report empirical regularities, or because the world is the way it is, from those general statements that are true because they

are conceptual *a prioris,* or because they represent a partial un-
packing of a given conceptual framework. The necessary continuity should be supplied by higher order propositions which
have an essential invariance with respect to conceptual transformations.

Ordinarily, the only way this covariance can be explicitated,
in cases where there is no series of ML propositions, is by a
rigorous reformulation of two conceptual systems so that they
can share, in part, a common metalanguage. Rather than attempt something this formal and formidable, I will settle for a
couple of illustrative examples.

One of the basic intellectual problems confronting primitive
man in every culture was a classification of the plants and
animals that constituted the principal features of his environment. As Claude Levi-Strauss, whose ideas I am adapting, has
pointed out, any system of classification, no matter how arbitrary or inadequate, is preferable to conceptual chaos.[28] Many
primitive groups, however, have developed elaborate and highly
precise systems of classification. Thus, cultural anthropologists
working with the Hunanóo tribe in the Southern Philippines
discovered that they could not master the terms in their language until they first learned enough botany and biology to distinguish the flora and fauna of the region. Even with such
prescientific classificatory systems, it is possible to formulate
many empirical generalizations which should carry over into
such practical sciences as agriculture, metallurgy, and medicine.
This, in fact, was the way these sciences developed, beginning
with the neolithic revolution.

The transition from a primitive classificatory system to a
contemporary scientific one is often a transition from a classificatory scheme based on sensible signs as criteria, e.g., the color
and odor of plants, to one based on rational signs. Thus, in the
Linnean system, the number of pistils in a plant determine the
order to which it is assigned while the number of stamens determine its class. This is a rational sign in that there is a de-
fensible reason for it: a recognition of the fact that plants

reproduce sexually, with the stamen as a male organ and the pistil as a female.

As empirical generalizations, if true, could carry over from a sensible to a rational classification, so too could they carry over from a macroscopic to a microscopic system of explanation. In discussing, for example, malaria macroscopically the disease is identified by its symptoms. This can lead to empirical generalizations, such as the fact that epidemics of malaria generally follow a rainy season. On a microscopic level malaria would be explained through a small parasitic protozoa transmitted by the anopheline mosquito. The empirical generalizations relating epidemics and climatic conditions would now be replaced by generalizations relating the transmission of the protozoa with the conditions necessary for the reproduction of the protozoa and its host vector, the mosquito that breeds in the stagnant water following the rainy season. In calling such a correspondence between two sets of empirical generalizations "covariance under conceptual transformation," the term 'covariance' loses its implication of precision. But it does serve to bring out the underlying continuity in the development of human thought as man, individually and collectively, seeks to express in language the reality of which he is a part, to borrow Bohr's favorite epistemological expression.

Perhaps some have become a bit lost with these technical terms and the attempt at precision. I will try to conclude this section by stating the basic ideas without the technical terms, though this inevitably involves a slight oversimplification. An empirical generalization may be spoken of as a law of nature. If such a law is true it does tell us something about nature. In this sense it corresponds to reality, but corresponds in a very special way.

If this series of lectures were to have a theme song, it would be "I'm always true to you, darling, in my fashion." Think for a minute of what is involved in representing such a tune in radically different media. It could exist as a pattern of sound vibrations, as a collection of inkmarks on a musical score, as wiggles in a wax groove, or as an ordered array of magnetic dipoles on a tape. If they all represent the same tune, they must all share the same form. The concrete embodiment of this form is necessarily different in the different media. But these embodiments must be interrelated by transformations which could be specified by rules (e.g., when you come across a certain mark on the musical score, strike a particular note on the piano). In this sense one might say that for a tune to remain invariant, i.e., to remain the same tune, its concrete embodiments must manifest an essential covariance.

Just as these media differ, so, too, do different conceptual systems, different ways of picturing and speaking about some aspect of reality. For these different frameworks to contain the same law, a law stating what obtains in reality, it is not necessary for the different expressions of the law to look the same or to give the same picture. Does a musical score look like the pattern of grooves in a record? But it is necessary for different expressions to share the same form. Since this is so, the fact that a particular empirical generalization is accepted as true does not guarantee the validity of the conceptualization in which it is embedded. All that is required for the truth of the empirical generalization is that the conceptualization supply an adequate basis for distinguishing and interrelating the properties or relations considered. It may be true in a stronger sense. But this stronger sense would mean either that factual claims stated in a particular PL are true, or that a particular conceptualization is considered a true theory, the next topic to be considered.

3. *Theoretical Statements*

Before discussing the truth of theoretical statements, we should clarify what we mean by 'theory.' For the way this term is used often predetermines, at least partially, the question of whether theoretical statements are reasonably accepted as true. Thus, in an instrumentalist view, a theory is basically just an inference mechanism leading from one set of factual claims to another. While the factual claims that launch or terminate the process of inference are candidates for the status of being true, the purely theoretical propositions are considered tools rather than statements of what obtains in reality. At the other extreme we have the classical tradition that interprets theories as explanatory systems involving deduction from premises that are true and known with certainty to be true. The spectrum of positions between these two extremes involves more complicated presuppositions on the truth-status of theories and theoretical statements.

What we must do, accordingly, is to try to specify what we mean by 'theory' in such a way that we do not predetermine the question of whether it is reasonable to call theories or theoretical statements true. What this calls for, I believe, is a quasi-phenomenological approach to scientific theories, something that will be outlined but not really developed here. One begins on an analytic descriptive level by determining how 'theory' functions and what sorts of things are called theories.[29] After isolating the sorts of things that are usually and reasonably called theories, one can proceed from descriptions of common features toward a specification of the underlying structure.

In principle this is what philosophers of science do in analyzing the logical structures and interpretative frameworks shared by scientific theories. Their practice, however, tends to rely much more on *a priori* considerations than on a descriptive analysis of functioning theories. The underlying presupposition for these *a priori* approaches is that any theory can be rationally reconstructed along the lines specified by contemporary logicians. Hence, in considering such problems as truth, empirical significance, explanation, and confirmation, one can rely on logical forms which, it is presumed, must be proper to the rational reconstruction of scientific theories. As I have attempted to show elsewhere,[30] this approach and the manner in which it is generally implemented tend to introduce serious distortions. Thus, it is difficult to think of any less likely vehicles for abiding truth-claims than Quine's eternal sentences. But with him, as with the Bob Jones Bible School, if you accept the system, you have to accept the idea that truth-claims are eternally identified with explicit formulations within a particular language.

Granted that theories do involve underlying logical structures, one means of analyzing these structures is—to adapt a term from current psychology—by analysis through synthesis. That is, a rational reconstruction of scientific theories which makes explicit the axioms, rules, and methods of interpretation does play an important, even a necessary, role in the philosophy of science. The only point I am insisting on, in criticizing much of what has been done along these lines, is that what is needed is a *re*construction rather than a fabrication from the whole cloth supplied by pure logic.

The structural description of scientific theories developed— or at least sketched—here involves two components, a physical language and a mathematical language. Under closer scrutiny, each component manifests a fine structure, and even a hyperfine structure. While these complications could be slighted earlier, they play a definite role in evaluating what is implied in accepting theoretical statements as true.

Within the physical language, the basic component is an extension of ordinary language involving a specification of the type of entities being discussed and a general conceptualization of the properties and relations attributed to these entities. This is not a theory in the technical sense but a background common to differing theories.

Thermodynamics affords a clear example of the role such a background system plays. Until scientists had developed adequate general concepts, general in the sense that they are indispensable for the description of observations, it was not possible to develop thermodynamics as a rigorous science.[31] But this background conceptual system does not form a theory in the technical sense of 'theory,' i.e., something that can be reduced to axiomatic form. To form such theories, further subdivision and specification are necessary. Tisza has worked this out for some operative scientific systems and has shown that thermodynamics must be considered a network of inter-related theories which share a common conceptual background and some common principles. But it is only particular sub-divisions, e.g., classical thermodynamics of equilibrium processes, that admit of a strict axiomatization.[32] This is the fine structure mentioned earlier. The hyperfine structure enters with the special assumptions distinguishing competing theories made within the same subdivision, though such differences are often more a question of mathematics than of physics.

Such a conceptualization including the fine structures generally precedes the formulation of a mathematical theory and serves as its interpretative base. Thus Faraday's qualitative explanation of electromagnetic fields preceded and was presupposed by Maxwell's mathematical theory of electromagnetism. Until Rutherford clarified the structure of the atom as electrons surrounding a tiny nucleus, no successful mathematical theory of the nucleus could be developed. This conceptualization that Rutherford developed was presupposed by the subsequent mathematical theories developed by Bohr, Schrödinger, Dirac and others. Theoretical nuclear physics had a similar career inasmuch as Chadwick's discovery of the neutron and Heisen-berg's explanation of the nucleus as a collection of protons and neutrons, rather than protons and electrons, was the necessary preliminary to developing an adequate mathematical formulation.

In addition to having an adequate physical conceptualization, one must also know, as a precondition for successful theory construction, the basic physical principles that obtain. Thus, the attempts to develop theories of fundamental particles presuppose conservation laws of mass-energy, electrical charge, linear momentum, angular momentum, baryon quantum number, strangeness quantum number, and isotopic spin. They also presuppose the basic validity of the quantum mechanical formalism, the laws of electromagnetic theory, and such general principles as relativistic covariance, causality, unitarity, and analyticity. I am not going to explain the technical meaning of these unfamiliar terms. The point I am making is that theory construction presupposes a background of established facts and general principles—what Hanson has called conclusions in search of a premise[33]—and that this background supplies an interpretative basis presupposed by differing theories. A particular theory not only adds a hyperfine structure to this physical conceptualization; it also provides a basis for a unified understanding of this otherwise rather disparate collection of facts and principles.

A mathematical formulation of the theory, particularly one done in a formal axiomatic fashion, does not admit of a corresponding decomposition into hierarchically ordered conceptual layers. Mathematical formulations have an "either-or" absoluteness to them. Thus, to take a current example, there are two theories of gravitation being contested at present, the theory of gravity (tensor theory) which grew out of Einstein's development of general relativity, and the Brans-Dicke (mixed scalar-tensor) theory which assumes a different mathematical form for the basic laws. The fact that the two theories share a network of background assumptions is reflected in the fact that they give approximately the same values for the same problems, e.g., shifts in the perihelions of planets. But *qua* mathematical systems they are simply and irreducibly different.

A physical theory, in the general sense of 'theory' that includes formulations in PL and ML and the correspondence between them, involves a background conceptualization, supplemented by specific assumptions, and a correlated set of mathematical formulations. In much of contemporary physics the mathematical formulation is the distinguishing feature of new theories, while the physical assumptions peculiar to the theory are those entailed by, or at least compatible with, a successful mathematical formulation. Thus, what was really novel about Dirac's relativistic quantum mechanics was what was implicit in his mathematical formulation, i.e., the existence of negative energy states and anti-particles.

Following current usage, we shall henceforth use the term

'theory' to refer to an organized body of scientific knowledge that can, in principle, be developed in a formal axiomatic fashion. However, we shall not assume that this axiomatic system constitutes a relatively isolated interpretative unit, but rather that it presupposes the type of layered background just outlined. Then the general question of the truth of scientific theories can be narrowed down to three more specific questions: (1) Should 'true' be predicated of scientific theories? (2) What is entailed in accepting theoretical statements as true? (3) What is the relation between the acceptance of theories and the truth of existence-claims concerning the entities postulated or presupposed by the theories?

(1) An opinion stemming from Karl Popper,[34] which seems to have won increasing acceptance,[35] is that, while theories may be called false, it is somewhat misleading to speak of them as true. The reason for this lack of symmetry is the logic of *modus tollens*. With the implication, "If p, then q," a denial of "q" entails a denial of "p," while an affirmation of "q" entails nothing. Confirmation and falsification of scientific theories follows this inference pattern. The premises coupled to the rules of reasoning entail a set of conclusions (an entailment which may be formulated as an implication). Experimental testing checks the truth of the conclusions. If the conclusions are false, the theory may be labeled 'false'; if the conclusions are true, the theory is not thereby established as true—unless one follows C. D. Broad's view that the fallacy of the consequent is the disgrace of logic and the glory of physics.

I believe that an analysis of the semantic categories proper to 'true' supports this evaluation. 'True' is primarily predicated of propositions but cannot be unambiguously extended to conceptual frameworks. Theories have a status intermediate between propositions and conceptual frameworks. In a strict axiomatic formulation one can make all the axioms into one proposition by linking them all together with 'ands.' But this would yield an uninterpreted formal calculus and blur the interesting differences in depth and significance which are generally one's focal concern in inquiring into the truth of an established theory. Inclusion of the interpretative base involves the type of conceptual background which we have been considering. The Popperian conclusion, accordingly, leads us over the threshold where we can confront the more complex question.

(2) Can theoretical statements be considered true? If some are accepted as true, to what degree does this entail acceptance of the different layers in the supporting conceptual framework? My view is that some theoretical statements are reasonably accepted as true, but that it is difficult to give a general characterization of such statements, because a host of complicating factors lead to too many differences. Prescinding temporarily from the really interesting case of the truth of existence-claims concerning theoretical entities, we may consider three different types of theoretical statements whose acceptance as true has somewhat different implications.

First, there are propositions initially proposed as hypotheses on theoretical grounds and eventually accepted as factual truths. Thus, "The earth is round," "Lightning is a discharge of atmospheric electricity" and "There are unstable particles whose mass is intermediate between that of a proton and an electron" are examples of statements first proposed as speculative hypotheses and now accepted as factual truths. To the degree that they become so accepted, they become a part of the conceptual background presupposed by more active theories. The boundary separating such factual claims from theoretical statements is somewhat arbitrary. I would tend to label as 'theoretical statements' any statements that are explicitly stated in the development of a theory and which serve as part of the base from which conclusions are deduced, while statements that are generally presupposed or which serve as part of the boundary conditions would be labeled 'factual claims.' Factual claims have already been considered. To call a theoretical statement of this sort 'true' is to imply that it is a candidate for such a status.

Secondly, there are factual claims that are deduced from

scientific theories so that their acceptability depends on the acceptability of the theory. Thus, as far as I know, no one has ever measured the wavelength of the radiation emitted when an electron makes a transition from the one hundred and first orbit to the hundredth orbit in the hydrogen atom. I cannot think of any good reason why anyone should want to make such a measurement. Yet, on the basis of some simple calculations, I am willing to affirm as a factual truth that this radiation has a wavelength of 4.623 cm. *Qua* factual claim this is no different from the claim that the radiation emitted in the transition from the second to the first orbit has a wavelength of 12.15 millionths of a cm. Yet the justification for the two claims is different. The second has been precisely measured, even before the development of the theory that yields it, while the first is accepted only because the theory gives this result.

It might seem that accepting such a conclusion as factually true entails accepting the theory that yields it as factually true. But this is based on a monolithic view of scientific theories. Something less total and more functional suffices. To see this we must analyze the logical processes by which such conclusions are inferred.

Theory-dependent physical implication manifests a complicated structure involving premises and conclusions in PL, a correspondence between predicates and propositions in PL and ML, and formal reasoning in ML. To schematize this we could use Latin letters for PL propositions, Greek letters for ML propositions, single-headed arrows with language-indicating subscripts for implication, and two-headed arrows for correspondence. Then theory-dependent physical implication would have the logical form:

1. $[(a_i \cdot c_j) \cdot (a_i \longleftrightarrow \alpha_i) \cdot (\alpha_i \underset{\text{ML}}{\longrightarrow} \beta_k) \cdot (\beta_k \longleftrightarrow b_k)] \underset{\text{PL}}{\longrightarrow} b_k$

To unpack (1), it states that from a conjunction of physical premises, a_i, boundary conditions, c_j, a correspondence between the PL premises, a_i, and a set of ML propositions, α_i, one may infer by the rules and principles proper to ML a set of mathematical conclusions, β_k. If there is a set of PL propositions, b_k, corresponding to β_k, then b_k is a set of theory-dependent physical implications of the initial premises and boundary conditions. This is developed in more detail elsewhere.[36]

The set of propositions, b_k, is in the same language and presupposes the same interpretative background as the sets a_i and c_j. Accepting b_k as factual truths entails accepting a_i and c_j as factual truths and vice versa. But it need not entail accepting α_i, the set of mathematical propositions, as factual truths. What is presupposed is that ML contains terms and propositions corresponding to the properties and relations specified in PL. This, in turn, requires the type of higher order isomorphism discussed earlier, with its theory-dependent and context-dependent conditions of correspondence. But it does not require that the formal principles of the ML system picture or correspond to physical reality in any direct sense. The second-order correspondence suffices.

This inference schema is routinely exemplified in the solution of any problem in quantum mechanics. Thus, one specifies the initial system plus the boundary conditions, translates these specifications into mathematical form by utilizing the correspondence between observables and operators, solves the resultant equations to get numerical conclusions, e.g., a set of eigenvalues, and then uses correspondence rules to translate these eigenvalue statements into statements about measurable values. The reasonable acceptance of such conclusions as factual truths need not imply that the basic propositions in ML are true in a correspondence sense. Schrödinger's Ψ-function does not correspond to physical reality in the way that the numerical conclusions correspond to measured values.

The final type of theoretical statement to be considered are general statements which are accepted as true in the sense of being laws of nature, rather than mere principles in accord with which one may infer true conclusions. Thus, the first and second laws of thermodynamics are accepted as true and cannot be explained away as mere conventions for the use of such terms as 'energy' and 'entropy.' Such statements differ from empirical generalizations in that they cannot be justified inductively, though inductive reasoning may suggest them. Yet, *qua* statements about physical reality, they are of the same nature as empirical generalizations. In calling such statements 'true,' one is predicating 'true' of an idealized generalization that functions as part of a tightly-knit conceptual framework. By the same sort of considerations employed earlier, one would conclude that the predication of 'true' entails covariance under conceptual transformations.

The significance of this requirement may be seen from the two examples cited. After Einstein established the equivalence of matter and energy, the law of the conservation of energy was promoted into a more general law of the conservation of mass-energy. Rudolph Clausius, who introduced 'entropy,' treated the law that entropy cannot decrease in any closed system as an absolute truth, though he later suspected that it had a statistical basis. Boltzmann's more fundamental interpretation of entropy as a statistical law (the Boltzmann H theorem) changed Clausius' absolute truth into a statistical truth. In both cases the general intent of the law was preserved, but the particular form in which the law was expressed changed when the fundamental concepts involved (energy, entropy) were understood in a different way.

(3) *Existence-Claims.* We are treating this topic separately because of the importance it has in recent philosophical defenses of scientific realism. Two aspects can be distinguished, only one of which is really problematic. The non-problematic aspect is the fact that the advancement of scientific thought has led to the acceptance of entities which are not directly observable. Tables of elements and charts of fundamental particles bear ample witness to this. The problematic aspect is the significance to be attached to this advance. Attempts to clarify this have involved a mélange of epistemological and ontological considerations that has undoubtedly generated more confusion than clarity. At the heart of all these efforts is the question of

accepting the truth and interpreting the significance of claims of the form, "There are Ns."

It is this, of course, that makes it our problem, but it is not ours in any exclusive sense. Though nature may not really abhor a vacuum, it rarely rewards any theorizing done in an intellectual or historical void. So let us begin this problem by considering the types of philosophical clarifications that have been given to existence claims within scientific theories.

The basic difficulty philosophers experienced in clarifying what the scientists had done centered around attempts to interrelate seeing and saying. Or, to be a bit more formal, there are two sorts of criteria for existence-claims whose interrelations have been a continuing source of controversy. One criterion is observability; seeing is believing. The other hinges on an analysis of the logical form of affirmed propositions. The emphasis on each pole came more from epistemological considerations than from attempts to analyze the practices actually operative in scientific advances.

In the first lecture we considered "bottom" and "middle of the page" interpretations of scientific theories (roughly equivalent to positivism and operationalism). Both tended to use some form of observability as a criterion of physical reality. Both experienced extreme difficulty in explaining the significance of existence-claims for theoretical entities. Either they were dismissed as useful fictions, or the distinction between 'theoretical' and 'observational' effectively became an ontological distinction between two types of entities. One is reminded of the sharp soul-body dualism which also represents, in my opinion, the transformation of a useful epistemological distinction (between perception and conceptualization) into a somewhat dubious ontological distinction that has formidable consequences.

The reaction against this involved a stress on logical form rather than observability as the criterion of ontic commitments. To schematize the pertinent arguments we could distinguish between phenomenological and substantive theories. If a theory postulates or presupposes a distinctive set of entities which are discussed within the theory, then it is a substantive theory. Such commitments can, in principle, be reduced to canonical form by a rational reconstruction of the theory along strictly axiomatic lines. Some of the axioms would be of the form $(\exists x)$ (Nx), where 'N' stands for a common noun predicate specifying the type of entities discussed. Then one who accepts this system as explanatory is logically committed to accept the existence of Ns, or of the entities whose names serve as the values of variables in these axioms.

Though I think that this approach has much to commend it in its acceptance of non-observable entities and its development of a critical realism, nevertheless there are difficulties which indicate the need for a change in this interpretation. First, phenomenological theories have led to the prediction and subsequent detection of new types of entities. The most striking recent example is the prediction of the Ω- meson on the basis of a group-theoretical (SU [3]) treatment of fundamental particles.

Secondly, this approach can lead to a lumping together of rather different types of ontic commitments, such as the particles of the physicist and the classes of the mathematician. This occurs both for the entities that are accepted, as parts of the furniture of the universe, and for those that are rejected, as Platonic abstract entities. The basis of this misleading juxtaposition is the type of univocal predication which is a necessary feature of any formal system based on a purely extensional logic. Thus, 'exist' must seem to have precisely the same meaning whether one says that numbers exist or that people exist. The operative difference is a difference between people and numbers, rather than a difference between two ways of existing.[37]

The third difficulty—and the one that induced me to modify this Quine-Sellars approach—is that this analysis does not really explicate the operative practice of scientists in deciding the acceptability of statements of the form, "There are Ns." Rather than impose a normative form inspired by logical and epistemological considerations, it would be better to begin by investigating the decision-procedures actually operative in scientific practice. Such an analysis would not obviate the need for a logical reconstruction, but it would be some guarantee that one would have a rational reconstruction rather than a mere imposition.

I am not going to attempt such a detailed analysis here. If anyone is looking for a dissertation topic in the philosophy of science, this would be an excellent one. What I would like to do, however, is to give enough of an outline of past and present entity-decisions to indicate how the truth and significance of statements of the form, "There are Ns," is decided.

We can begin with the acceptance of atoms and molecules. The usual philosophical argument is to the effect that acceptance of kinetic theory as explanatory entailed acceptance of molecules in motion as real. The actual history was a bit more complicated. In the mid-nineteenth century there were atomists and energetists and conflicting groups within each division. Virtually all these scientists would accept kinetic theory as explanatory, at least after the theory was adequately developed. But Ostwald, Mach, Duhem and other leaders of the *Energetik* school argued that this did not entail the acceptance of atoms as real existents. In addition to the philosophical differences separating the two schools, there was a fundamental disagreement over whether nature is ultimately discontinuous (the atomists) or continuous.

A series of developments between 1890 and 1909 (when Ostwald announced his conversion to atomism) supplied independent evidence both for discontinuity in nature and for the real existence of atoms and particles. Cathode rays were explained in terms of electrons. There were converging determinations of Avogardro's number (the number of molecules in a certain volume of gas) by differing means. Gibbs' work on kinetic theory became known and was advanced by Boltzmann in such a way that kinetic theory went beyond classical thermodynamics in its explanations. Planck explained radiation in terms of quanta, though radiation had been the prime example of continuity in nature. Einstein used the idea of atoms to explain Brownian motion, and Jean Perrin extended Einstein's considerations as a basis for estimating the size of water molecules. With so much evidence the proposition, "There are atoms," could be detached from any particular theory—since Dalton's time there have always been competing atomic theories—and asserted as factually true.

The presently accepted lists of particles and classes of particles include many that were first discovered experimentally and then identified: e.g., the neutron, and others that were first introduced as theoretical postulates. Our concern is with the question of when the latter type were accepted as real, rather than hypothetical, entities. Such an appraisal of acceptance on the part of the scientific community inevitably involves a subjective judgment on my part. However, I do not think that there would be serious disagreement to most of the judgments.

When Pauli postulated the neutrino in 1930, it was looked on as an *ad hoc* hypothesis to save the principle of energy conservation in explanations of beta decay. After Fermi developed a mathematical theory of beta decay, in which Pauli's assumption played a key role, the existence of the neutrino gradually came to be accepted. It was an assumption that was necessary to explain various types of particle decays, for example, the mu-meson, and played a role in other conservation laws besides energy. Physicists, accordingly, had little hesitation about including the neutrino in lists of fundamental particles even prior to its experimental detection by Reines and Cowan. This was brought out in a very dramatic way at a theoretical physics meeting in St. Louis in 1957. Reines (or Cowan) summarized the monumental and extremely expensive experiments that led to the actual detection of neutrinos. From an analysis of these experiments he concluded that the collision cross-section for the neutrino did not fit the two-component theory of the neutrino which Lee and Yang had just introduced as a consequence of their discovery of parity non-conservation in weak interactions. T. D. Lee, who had already given two papers at the meeting and whose ideas dominated the conference, was asked to comment. He stated that if the experiments did not fit his theory of the neutrino, then the experiments must be wrong and should be done over. The experiments were done over at a considerable cost in time, money, and manpower; finally the conclusions that Lee had predicated were reached.[38]

Both mesons and anti-particles were first predicted on theoretical grounds, but not accepted as real until they were discovered experimentally. The case of anti-particles is rather interesting. In his original paper on the relativistic theory of the electron, Dirac said that he hoped to find some way of getting rid of the negative energy solutions. When they proved to be an inescapable ontic commitment of the theory, he devised his famous interpretation of an infinite sea of negative energy with anti-particles as holes in that sea. Few physicists took it seriously until Anderson discovered the positron experimentally in 1932.[39] By the mid-1950's the theories that demanded the existence of anti-particles, corresponding to Fermi-Dirac particles, had proved so successful that physicists concluded that there should be anti-protons and anti-neutrons. Yet, statements of their existence were not accepted as true (rather than probable) until they were experimentally detected: the anti-proton by Chamberlain, Segre *et al.*, in 1955, and the anti-neutron by Cork *et al.* in 1956.

The number of particles and resonance states accepted in contemporary physics is roughly a function of the United States national budget. Whenever the government allocates enough money to build newer and higher energy accelerators, new particles are discovered. But, in addition to these particles which are detected experimentally and which fit into the now familiar classes of leptons, mesons, and baryons, there are other types of particles whose existence is postulated or simply speculated on theoretical grounds. The current attempts to detect such particles bear witness to the unwillingness of physicists to accept such entities as real simply on the grounds that they are ontic commitments of theories accepted as explanatory.

A list of such theoretical entities, roughly in order of decreasing likelihood, would include: *the intermediate boson,* which should have a mass greater than 2 Bev. and a lifetime less than 10^{-16} sec., postulated as a basis of weak interactions; *quarks and antiquarks,* entities with a one-third unit electrical charge and a heavy mass, relative to the mass of the proton, which a group-theoretical treatment of strong interactions postulates as constituting baryons (3 quarks) and heavy mesons (a quark and an antiquark); *tachyons,* the faster than light particles postulated by Bilaniuk and Sudarshan; *spurions,* particles which seem to be implied by Regge-pole treatments of high energy interactions; and *chimerons,* which Gell-Mann postulated as constituent of weak interactions corresponding to the role of quarks in strong interactions.[40]

From a physicist's point of view these theoretical entities have rather different statuses. Some are implicit in theories already accepted; others are merely compatible with such theories. From an epistemological point of view they share a common feature. The relevant theories could be rationally reconstructed to include axioms of the form, $(\exists x)(Nx)$, where 'N' names the entities in question.[41] But in none of the cases considered is the statement, "There are Ns," accepted as true, rather than more or less probable, simply on the grounds that 'Ns' are implicit in theories that are accepted as explanatory. In any treatment, such as the present one, that links 'true' with the acceptance of propositions, this is a crucial consideration.

The conclusions I draw from this admittedly superficial survey are rather tentative. Let us return to the idea of a scientific system interpreted in terms of a physical language and a mathematical language. In PL we can distinguish a hierarchy of interpretative assumptions. It is convenient to distinguish three layers, previously referred to as a basic structure, a fine structure, and a hyperfine structure. These are roughly equivalent to: a basic descriptive metaphysics implicit in the language used, a metaphysics that specifies which types of things are spoken of as basic (things, events, fields . . .) and what sorts of properties are attributed to them; a set of background presuppositions concerning factual claims and general principles shared by otherwise competing theories in a given domain; and the special assumptions that characterize a *particular* theory. If particular theories involve changes in background assumptions, then one has a conceptual revolution, whether major or minor, and a different fine structure supporting the hyperfine structure.

The question of whether or not postulated theoretical entities should be accepted as real is a practical physical question, not a metaphysical question. Its answer depends on acceptance by a scientific community and not on a metaphysical theory of the act of existence. I believe that it reduces to the question of whether or not the proposition, "There are Ns," can be detached from particular theories and considered a part of the background assumptions, or fine structure, proper to a domain which otherwise competing theories, actual or possible, must accept, or whether this proposition is an assumption proper to one particular theory, or part of the hyperfine structure. Only if the proposition can be detached from particular theories can it be considered as an existential claim that is accepted as true by the scientific community. This possibility of detachment is a question of principle rather than practice and depends on the way the scientific community understands and evaluates a theory. Thus, in the early 1930's, Dirac's theory of relativistic quantum mechanics was the only theory predicating anti-particles. Later, when the idea of anti-particles was accepted, Dirac's idea of anti-particles as holes in a negative energy sea was supplemented by two other ideas: Feynman's idea of anti-particles as ordinary particles going backward in time, and the very formal interpretation associated with creation and annihilation operators. All three interpretations support the same mathematical and observational conclusions.

In this evaluative judgment on the part of the scientific

community, two general criteria seem to be operative, though more in an intuitive than in a formal way. First, there should be some evidence for the existence of the entities in question independent of their role in a particular theory. Ideally, this evidence is experimental detection. But if this cannot be had, there should be something which can count as supporting evidence over and above the role the entities play in the particular theory. An illustrative example is the role of the neutrino in explaining various types of weak interactions and in supporting different conservation laws, or the success of the formalism involving particle—anti-particle symmetry in quantum electrodynamics. Secondly, if the entity is not detected experimentally, there should be adequate reasons to explain why this non-detection is expected—for example, because of the very low probability that a neutrino will interact with anything, or the high energy required to produce anti-protons, or the short lifetime and high mass of the intermediate vector boson, etc.

An axiomatic formulation aims at, though it cannot completely achieve, completeness and consistency. To achieve completeness all pertinent details have to be specified. This implies that what is axiomatized is necessarily a *particular* theory in the sense in which we have been using the term: all three levels rather than just the first two. The levels as such do not come through since an explicit axiomatization necessarily democratizes the hierarchial ordering of assumptions proper to PL. Accordingly, in an axiomatic reformulation of a theory, any propositions of the form, "There are Ns," necessarily functions as part of a particular theory. If what seems to be the same axiom occurs in a different theory, it cannot have the same meaning. This is because a strict axiomatization implicitly defines the syntactical meaning, though not the interpretation, of the primitive terms. Any change in an axiom or rule involves a change in the meaning of *all* the terms defined within the system, whether implicitly or explicitly defined. Such a purely formal approach, accordingly, is incapable of clarifying the factors that explicate the meaning and justify the acceptance of existential propositions on the part of the scientific community. I know of no way in which one can retain such a formal approach and still detach such existential propositions from particular theories.

In the last lecture we attempted to bring out the relation between judgment, truth, and existential claims. The judgment, grounded in a reflective grasp of reasons sufficient to warrant assent to the proposition considered as a hypothesis, adds a contribution to knowing distinct from the contributions of experience and understanding. Existential claims depend on propositions affirmed or accepted as factual truths, and this affirmation, in turn, depends on judgment. A detailed consideration of a concrete and presently controverted case has brought us back to the same consideration. An evaluative judgment on the part of the scientific community accepting "There are Ns" as a proposition which may, in principle, be detached from a particular theory and affirmed as true is the basis for saying that Ns are real, rather than hypothetical or possible, entities. Such claims are not metaphysical claims—but they are the type of claims which the metaphysician ignores only at the risk of developing a metaphysics of being which will become increasingly irrelevant in a scientific world.

IV

TRUTH
IN THEOLOGY

This lecture, more than any of the preceding ones, stands in need of a preliminary clarification. I will be covering a lot of territory, but covering it from a very limited perspective. Unless these sharp, self-imposed limitations are kept in mind it will be easy to misunderstand the significance of what I am saying and doing. I will be considering the truth of theological propositions, but my approach will be *analytical* rather than confessional. I will not try to determine which theological propositions, if any, should be accepted as true. I will simply be inquiring into what is involved in accepting any theological propositions as true.

I

The Role of Theological Propositions

Logically, it might seem that we should begin with the question of the meaningfulness of religious language. If theological or religious statements have no meaning, then there is little point or purpose in examining their truth-value. It might seem that I should begin there—but I will not. All that I intend to do here is to indicate the state of the question and the reasons

129

why I am skimming over it. The first reason is the fact that I will be treating this problem elsewhere.[1] The second reason is the fact that I personally find the on-going discussion on the meaningfulness of religious language rather banal and unenlightening.

The recent tradition began with John Wisdom's article, "Gods," and the further development of Wisdom's ideas by Flew.[2] By focusing on a simple parable concerning a cultivated patch in the wilderness and the hypothetical gardener who may or may not be attending to it, Wisdom and Flew argue that simple literal theism is meaningful but untenable while qualified literal theism is meaningless. A literal theist is one who claims that God really exists. A qualified literal theist admits this, but then hastens to add that God is invisible, atemporal, has no spatial location, cannot be perceived or directly known, etc. The net result, in the opinion of Wisdom, Flew, and others, is that the concept of God has died the death of a thousand qualifications. This leads to the conclusion that theological statements should be given a non-cognitive interpretation as expressions of emotion or subjective attitude.

On one level there is no real question about the meaningfulness of religious language. Believers can understand each other quite readily. Theologians turn out hundreds of books and thousands of articles each year—and not all of these are unintelligible. This, in itself, does not prove much. Believers in astrology, in ESP, in poltergeists, and in flying saucers can also communicate meaningfully with their fellow believers. The distinction between meaning and reference implies that religious language could be meaningful even if God did not exist. A referential theory of meaning is no more helpful in clarifying religious or theological language than it is in explicating other forms of language.

The Ayer-Wisdom-Flew tradition did not really analyze religious language, the way people actually use language to express and develop their theological convictions. What was really operative was a theory concerning the meaningfulness of empirical language, its nature, grounds, and limits. To use such a theory as the basis for judging the meaningfulness of religious language is reasonable only if one has already established that the theory in question is an adequate basis for clarifying the meaningfulness of language in general. As noted in the last lecture, ordinary language analysis cannot cope with the extended use of language proper to science unless special consideration is given to the problem of the extension of ordinary language frameworks to new domains. No amount of ordinary language analysis can ever settle the question of the existence of quarks, or even make a significant contribution to this discussion. Until the authors in question develop an adequate explanation of how language is extended to discuss entities that transcend an ordinary language framework, they have not really raised the question in a manner that admits of a meaningful answer, whether positive or negative.[3]

There is a further point, one which has been more or less setting the tone for these lectures. In his later works, Wittgenstein brought out the importance of considering language when it is functioning rather than when it is idling. I have tried to adhere to this when considering extended uses of language. Thus an adequate clarification of the meaning and use of scientific statements must eventually go beyond considerations of what a logician might possibly mean when he formulates sentences about crows that are black, swans that may be white, and emeralds that are green for the time being, and analyze what a scientist actually means when he speaks about atoms, or genes, or the gross national product. Similarly, an analysis of the actual use and functioning of religious language must eventually go beyond a consideration of what an Oxbridge don might possibly mean were he to utter a belief-like statement, or a fideistic linguistic performative. Eventually one must consider how theological language actually functions. This is crucial in the present context of analyzing the meaning and implications of labeling a theological proposition 'true.' In the second lecture we emphasized the point that 'true,' as a functioning term, is closely linked to asserting and accepting propositions. Such acceptance is part of the way of life of an individual and an on-going community. Accordingly, we shall concentrate on the way propositions are asserted and accepted within religious groups, specifically within the Christian tradition, rather than on linguistic specimens antiseptically detached from a living environment.[4]

Though my approach will be analytic rather than confessional, I wish to focus on the Christian tradition. There are some obvious reasons for this choice: our shared commitments; my limited knowledge of other religious traditions; my hope of contributing something to contemporary theological discussions. But there is also another reason of a rather different sort: the suitability of the subject matter. This is due to the unique role that understanding and truth have played in the Christian tradition. As Randall, the eminent historian of intellectual history, put it:

No other culture has assigned so central a place to religious beliefs, and in no other has the refinement and criticism of primitive religious practices been so concerned with knowledge and understanding. Elsewhere the working over of religious materials has normally been moral and imaginative or artistic, not intellectual. . . . This imaginative lore has normally not been taken as "correct" of binding doctrine, but rather as something to be enjoyed and used, as the religious teacher uses parables, to point a moral or symbolize an ideal.

But characteristically, Christianity has always seen itself as a faith, and despite both Jesus and Paul faith soon came to mean correct or orthodox beliefs about God and man and human destiny. In sharp contrast, for both Judaism and Islam, religion has never been a faith to be believed, but rather a law to be followed. For Buddhism and Hinduism, it has been a way or a path of life to be pursued; for Confucianism, a code or standard of conduct to be observed.[5]

No group within the Christian tradition has ever laid as much stress on the truth of propositions as Roman Catholicism.

For centuries the Church has been defining doctrines and insisting that acceptance of the truth of every defined doctrine is
an essential condition for full membership in the Church. Anyone wishing to analyze what is involved in accepting theological
propositions as true could hardly imagine a better case—or a
more plentiful source of problems. To see something of the
problems this involves, let us consider a collection of statements, each of which was put forward as an orthodox formulation of the central doctrine of the Christian tradition, the divinity of Christ.

St. John the Evangelist (Jn. 1, 14): "And the Word *became*
flesh and dwelt among us," a statement which clearly implies
the pre-existence of Christ.

St. Peter's statement (Acts 2, 36): "Let the house of Israel
know assuredly that God has *made* him both Lord and Christ,
this Jesus whom you crucified," does not carry any implication
of pre-existence.

Nor does St. Paul's (Rom. 1, 3): ". . . the gospel concerning
his Son, who was descended from David according to the flesh
and *designated* Son of God in power according to the Spirit of
holiness by his resurrection from the dead, Jesus Christ our
Lord."

St. Cyril of Alexandria, whose formulation of Christological
theses was accepted and defined by the Council of Ephesus,
expressed his characteristic views in a letter: "We say that the
two natures are united, but that after the union there is no
longer a division into two [natures]; we believe therefore in
one nature of the Son, because he is one, though become man
and flesh."[6]

Twenty years after Cyril's death, the Council of Chalcedon
issued a solemn decree: "One and the same Christ, Son, Lord,
only-begotten, made known in *two natures* [which exist] without confusion, without change, without division, without separation; the difference of the natures having been in no wise
taken away by reason of the union, but rather the properties of
each being preserved."[7]

St. Thomas Aquinas gave a lapidary expression of what he accepted as the central core of the Christian tradition: "If therefore human nature was not united to the word of God in a person, it was not united to it in any way."[8]

Leslie Dewart, a contemporary Catholic trained in the Thomistic tradition, expressed this doctrine somewhat differently: ". . . no Christian believer today (except as noted) can intelligently believe that in one hypostasis of Jesus *two* real natures are united. . . . If, on the contrary, he was only a divine person, he was not true man."[9]

In a recent encyclical Pope Paul reaffirmed the traditional formulation: "He is the Eternal Word, born of the Father before time began, and one in substance with the Father, *homoousios to Patri;* and through him all things were made."[10]

Ansgar Hulsbosch, a Dutch Catholic theologian, gave a somewhat different formulation: "The divinity of Christ consists in the perfection of his humanity."[11]

To accept as valid the conceptual framework in which any one of these statements is embedded while denying the truth of the particular statement is to deny the divinity of Christ. To affirm them all as true in a maximal sense, the propositions along with their framework presuppositions, entails affirming contradictory propositions. One way out of this dilemma, one which Pope Paul has strongly encouraged, is to accept one formulation, the officially approved one, as normative of true orthodoxy.[12] This solution, unfortunately, is inadequate to the problem. Maintaining a theological formulation is no guarantee that one is maintaining the same theological proposition. It is rather easy to give examples of formulations that have remained while their meanings changed.

Thus, in repeating the Creed, the pious Christian affirms that "Christ descended into hell." This is quite meaningful in terms of a three-tiered cosmos: the earth in the middle, heaven above, and hell below, with hell subdivided into a waiting room for those who are not condemned but are not yet saved and the abode of the damned. Whatever this regularly repeated affirmation may mean today, it certainly does not mean that.[13] St. Cyprian's phrase, *"Extra ecclesiam nulla salus,"* was accepted by the Church Fathers and rather grimly interpreted in terms of membership in the institutionalized Church as a necessary condition for salvation. Both Vatican II and Pope Paul's encyclical on the Church clearly taught the opposite. The Church still retains the statement as official teaching but gives a radically different interpretation to "outside the Church." Other instances could easily be developed: the meaning attached to 'creation' before and after the acceptance of a doctrine of evolution; Boniface VIII's solemn declaration on the absolute necessity of submission to the Pope as a condition for salvation; the Council of Trent's statements on the role of one couple in original sin; the condemnation of usury as immoral by medieval ecumenical councils. In these and other instances, the formulation defined, or at least accepted, by the Church remains the official doctrine. But the *meaning* attached to such formulations is not fixed by the formulations themselves. It depends on the role these propositions play in current discussions or, to adopt the jargon, in theological language games. This role has effectively, sometimes radically, changed.

An attempt to analyze what is entailed in accepting such statements as true leads to two related problems. The first is the problem of the relation of the meaningfulness of a proposition both to a conceptual framework and to the role it plays within that framework. Though this problem has already been discussed in varying forms, we have not yet investigated either the distinctive assumptions underlying theological discourse or the unique role that theological propositions may play as vehicles of an abiding communal commitment. The second problem, one adumbrated in the examples just cited, is the significance of conceptual revolutions in conditioning the meaningfulness of statements accepted as true. This has a peculiar significance in theology, where a statement need not be understood to be accepted as true. Both the theological idea of mystery and the ecclesiastical idea of authority induce believers to accept as true propositions whose real meaning they do not grasp.

A suggestive point of departure is a comparison between the three types of propositions considered in the discussion of science (factual claims, empirical generalizations, and theoretical statements), and a theological trichotomy (scriptural claims, creedal or conciliar affirmations, and theoretical statements). A supplementary benefit of this parallelism is that it serves as a means of yoking a chronological treatment of doctrinal development to a systematic treatment of different types of theological propositions. The shortcomings of this parallelism will gradually become more obvious. But it should not be discarded until we have extracted whatever insight it has to offer.

II

TRUTH IN SCRIPTURE

Factual claims (The cat is on the mat) and scriptural affirmations (Jesus is Lord) have radically different functions. Yet the acceptance of each has an *a priori* grounding not exhibited by other types of statements considered. Thus, one is committed *a priori* to accepting as true any statements that correspond to the facts, though this general commitment does not in itself determine either what facts are or what it means to conform to them. Similarly, the orthodox believer is committed *a priori* to accepting as true whatever Scripture teaches, though this acceptance does not determine what it means for Scripture to teach anything.

In spite of this parallelism in function there must be an anti-parallelism in method. In analyzing ordinary language— *our* ordinary language—it is reasonable to begin with individual sentences and gradually work toward conceptual frameworks. This is reasonable because the underlying conceptualization and its framework features have already been absorbed. The problem is to make these implicit features explicit. But this same method can prove disastrous as an approach to a radically different framework. If, in studying the written records of a different culture, we begin with individual sentences and ignore the general conceptual background, we will end with an explication of what *we* would have meant had we made such assertions. But the point and purpose of exegesis is to understand what the original author meant. Hence, the appropriate methodology is that specified by the famous hermeneutic circle. The individual elements in a complex cannot be understood without some grasp of the whole. But an articulation of these elements is the only means of correcting and deepening our understanding of the whole.

Here, however, we are attempting to do epistemology, not exegesis. Accordingly, I will try, in a schematic way, to translate the work of exegetes into epistemological terms. Recent research into documents of the early Christian era, such as the scrolls from Qumran (Jewish milieu) and Nag-Hammadi (Judaeo-Christian milieu) as well as form criticism of the Scriptures themselves, is making it increasingly clear that the New Testament writings represent the result of a considerable process of doctrinal development within the early Church. This Church was at least as divided as our present Church between conservatives and progressives. The conservatives were the Judaeo-Christians, Palestinian Christians led by James the Apostle, who combined a Christian faith with a loyalty to traditional Jewish customs, forms of worship, and attitudes— including opposition to Rome. This was the dominant group in the early Church, with the progressive movement of pagan Christianity, initiated by Stephen and eventually led by Paul, essentially a fringe element. After the destruction of Jerusalem in 70 A.D. and the dispersal of the Judaeo-Christians, the pagan Christians gradually achieved dominance. After the second unsuccessful Jewish revolt against Rome (140 A.D.), there was a strong reaction against Judaeo-Christianity. The tattered remnants of the once dominant conservative group took more extreme forms (Millenarism, Encratism, and Ebionism) and

were labeled as heretics by the now dominant Pauline Christians.[14]

The New Testament Scriptures were shaped almost exclusively by the progressive wing of the Church and geared to the
needs of the Gentile Christians. However, the literary forms
employed often reflected the Jewish background of those who
shaped the oral and later written teaching, e.g., the adoption
of midrashes, of rabinical casuistry, of allegories, of Old Testament excerpts used in accommodated senses, etc. It seems likely
that none of the Gospel accounts as we now have them were
written by eye-witnesses. Though the historical Jesus is the
nuclear core of the events and doctrine presented, the emphasis
is on the Christ of faith. The individual authors selected, arranged, and interpreted the available material in accord with
purposes that were theological, ecclesiastical, and personal. The
literary forms they employed were quite different from those
we are accustomed to. They did not, in particular, intend to
present historical recitals, in Von Ranke's sense of objectively
recording the facts as they actually happened.[15]

These ideas are probably familiar to anyone conversant with
contemporary Scripture studies. I am not attempting to replace
the exegete, but to probe the epistemological significance of his
work. Accordingly, I willingly relinquish to the experts the real
work involved in *Formgeschichte* and *Redaktionsgeschichte* and
will give an epistemological interpretation of their work by
distinguishing three different conceptual levels which condition
the meaningfulness of the propositions asserted in the New
Testament.

*Level One: The Theological Orientation of the Individual
Author or Redactor.* Though the distinguishing attributes and
particular purposes of an author cannot always be sharply specified, yet there are clear differences in the way the same basic
source material is arranged and used. Thus, Mark's Gospel
concentrates on Christ's struggle with the powers of darkness;
Matthew's is characterized by his implicit emphasis on the
Church and the role of faith; Luke's Gospel has a characteristic

stress on personal encounter with Jesus through faith and on the universality of salvation wrought by Jesus; the Gospel attributed to John emphasizes Christ's divinity.

Level Two: A Common Interpretative Background. The authors of the New Testament accounts never intended an historical recital for its own sake. Each was presenting a theological interpretation of Jesus. But what they wrote was essentially a functional theology.[16] What Jesus is was understood in terms of what he did, while what he did was understood in terms of an interpretation of divine activity stemming from Old Testament themes. God had redeemed the Jews by bringing them out of their bondage in Egypt, had formed a covenant with them, giving them a law and making them his people, and then had led them into the promised land. Similarly, Jesus' life, death, and resurrection were interpreted as salvific acts on a universal scale which redeemed mankind from its bondage to sin, formed a new covenant between man and God through the new law of the Spirit, unified mankind (at least potentially) by making all people his people, and opened to men the gates of the kingdom of heaven, the ultimate land of promise.

Level Three: An Underlying Conceptualization. Scripture scholars have drawn attention to those aspects of the Semitic conceptualization that differ from our own: e.g., in views of the cosmos, of man as an animated body rather than a soul inhabiting a body, in the concept of time, in the absence of contemporary concepts of physical laws, etc. What we wish to consider here are not these particular features of the author's *Weltanschauung,* but the role that any such conceptualization plays in the affirmation of truth.

To get at this, let us assume, somewhat idealistically, that a community of Scripture scholars considering the factors enumerated have reached agreement on the exegesis and interpretation of a certain section of Scripture, e.g., the infancy narrative in Matthew's Gospel. Suppose that they conclude, *inter alia,* that the author of Matthew was teaching that Jesus' coming was the fulfillment of God's promise to send a Savior. A simplistic application of the ideas developed earlier would suggest that this is the proposition, or scriptural claim, that the author was affirming as true.

Even this first approximation to a truth-claim requires qualifications. First, the author's primary purpose was not to affirm propositions in a textbook sense, but to proclaim a saving event. Secondly, to extract a candidate for the status of an affirmed proposition we have to transpose the Gospel account into our own terms. To claim that this was what the author intended to say is rather misleading. What he intended to say was what he did in fact say—the Gospel account as written. The propositional transcription embodies our understanding of what he said. These qualifications, however, need not prove an insurmountable obstacle. If the exegetical interpretation is correct, it is reasonable to presume that the original author, confronted with this proposition and understanding the purpose of the confrontation, would accept the proposition as true —though he would undoubtedly qualify it as inadequate.

Suppose, *ex absurdo,* that this exegetical process were carried to completion, that the exegete was really able to put on the mind of Matthew, of John, of Paul, etc., understand exactly what the original authors meant, and transpose these statements into equivalent claims in our conceptual framework. Would such an idealized cross-cultural understanding settle all questions concerning the theological truths taught by Scripture? I believe that the answer to this question must be a clear and unequivocal "No." To put on the mind of Matthew is to assume the conceptual limitations of Matthew. Though he may have had a clear idea of what he wished to affirm, he could not, from within his own conceptual framework, specify the ontic boundaries of his affirmations. Though Matthew might relate wonders, he could not affirm that an event transcended laws of nature without a conceptual framework in which 'laws of nature' is a meaningful expression. If his concept of man lacked a distinction between 'person' and 'nature,' he could not affirm that Christ was one person with two natures, though he could reveal what Christ is through what he did and said. When we ask questions such as: "Did Matthew affirm the real existence of angels?" or "Did Mark affirm the devil theory of epilepsy?", we are asking questions that are meaningful in our framework, rather than theirs. If more precise distinctions, more adequate conceptual systems, and a clearer understanding of what it means to give an explanation are indispensable tools in articulating and affirming the nature of the real, then there is a moral necessity of going beyond the formulations of Scripture, or of the exegete's paraphrase of Scripture, to come to a fuller and truer grasp of the reality revealed. In theology, as in any other branch of human knowledge, the development of doctrine is necessitated by the very thrust of the human mind toward a more adequate understanding of what is.

The nature of the ensuing doctrinal development is often misunderstood because of an absolutist interpretation of the significance of theological truth claims. As Avery Dulles explained it in an excellent article on dogma and doctrinal development:

This process of reinterpretation cannot be a matter of stripping away the human conceptual vesture until one reaches some timeless and unquestionable kernel of pure divine truth. The pursuit of such an unconditioned grasp of revelation is an illusion, betraying a serious ignorance of man's fundamental historicity. We ourselves are just as historically conditioned as our ancestors, and hence cannot hope to achieve supracultural formulations.[17]

The contrast between the full acceptance of man's culturally conditioned historicity and the search for the particular propositional formulations that express the timeless kernel of divine truth is apparent in the difference between the actual historical development of doctrinal formulation and the neo-Scholastic interpretation accorded these formulations. Such official dogmatic pronouncements as creedal statements and conciliar decrees were interpreted—through a fusion of the Scholastic notion of truth as correspondence, an ahistorical view of the Church, and a juridical and monarchical view of the doctrinal role of ecclesiastical authority—as identical with revelation, as possessing conceptual objectivity, as immutable, and as universal in significance. As Dulles clearly shows, actual formulations of doctrines have never had these attributes or played this role.

III

CREEDAL AFFIRMATIONS AND CONCILIAR DECREES

Reliance on formulation-fixity is out. But simple relativism is not a viable alternative. Creedal statements and conciliar decrees have played a unique role in the Church's expression of what it is and believes. Though these are not, as conservative Catholicism would have it, a linguistic transcription of a divinely imparted system of universal and timeless truths entrusted to the Church as custodian and teacher, neither are they formulations which may simply be dismissed as outdated. Our concern here is not to determine which statements should be accepted as true, but to understand the distinctive status such truth-claims enjoy. Before attempting to analyze this, we will present a brief historical sketch which should serve to anchor the analysis.[18]

To make the discussion more concrete we will generally focus on one problem, the one that has played a central role in the development of Christian doctrine and which seems predestined to become the glowing core of coming controversies. The question is: Who is Jesus of Nazareth? The history of Christianity has witnessed a series of answers to this. What we wish to consider is what is entailed in accepting both an on-going tradition, as an expression of the Church's gradual clarification and articulation of this doctrine, and a particular formulation, e.g., the Council of Chalcedon, as an authoritative statement of this central truth.

As noted earlier, New Testament Christology is essentially functional. The Old Testament did not attempt to explain God in ontological terms. He is presented, to use G. Ernest Wright's apposite phrase, as "He who acts," the one who calls Abraham, inspires Moses, chooses a people, speaks through the prophets, and rewards and punishes his people. Similarly, the New Testament presents its distinctive revelation in terms of divine actions. The Father sends his Son into the world as its redeemer; the Son returns to the Father and they send forth the Holy Spirit to extend Christ's salvific work. Because of this functional action-centered view, there was no attempt to develop a consistent conceptualization of how the relation of God and man in Christ is to be understood. The earliest accounts tend to speak of Christ's divinity as something gradually realized through a process culminating in the resurrection. Following Grillmeier,[19] it is possible to distinguish five different scriptural formulations of the divine and human in Christ: the Son of God *becomes* man (Gal. 4, 4; Rom. 1, 3; Phil. 2, 7); he *gives* up, in some fashion, his divinity to *take on* our humanity (Phil. 2, 7); the fullness of the divinity *dwells in* him corporeally (Col. 1, 19; 2, 9); he *appears* or *is manifested* in the flesh (1 Tim. 3, 16; Tit. 2, 11; 3, 4; 1 Jn. 1, 2); he *is* the Word who *is* God (Jn. 1, 1).

These conceptual inconsistencies were not an immediate cause of concern for the earliest Christians. Their problem was one of survival and growth. They counted few philosophers among their numbers, and even those with a philosophical background would accept St. Paul's teaching that the wisdom of the world is folly before God. Yet a variety of factors contributed to change this. Three motives in particular drove the early Church in the direction of doctrinal development.[20]

First, there was an apologetic motive, the need to express Christian truth in a form that would meet the requirements and answer the objections of the surrounding world. For both Jewish and Greek critics, the basic objections which these apologists must meet concerned the divinity of Christ. As Celsus, an early critic, formulated the basic objection, Christians who worship Christ are either guilty of worshiping a man or they have abandoned monotheism.

Secondly, there was the problem of heresy, of ideas put forward as Christian doctrine which did not seem to accord with the truth of the Gospel. Even in retrospect, the bitterness engendered by accusations of heresy is difficult to understand. These controversies have a peculiar bearing on any evaluation of the significance of the conciliar formulations they occasioned. Many of the central ideas of Christian revelation were not given a precise formulation on the grounds that they were mysteries which were incomprehensible and ineffable. However, a heretical formulation of such a mystery could only be countered by a less misleading formulation. And so the Fathers of the Church were gradually coerced into attempting to give a precise formulation to doctrines which their predecessors had claimed to be incapable of being expressed in any human formulation. St. Hilary expressed their dilemma very vividly:

The errors of heretics and blasphemers force us to deal with unlawful matters, to scale perilous heights, to speak unutterable words, to trespass on forbidden ground. Faith ought in silence to fulfill the commandments, worshiping the Father, reverencing with him the Son, abounding in the Holy Spirit, but we must strain the poor resources of our language to express thoughts too great for words. The error of others compels us to err in daring to embody in human terms truths which ought to be hidden in the silent veneration of the heart.[21]

Theology manuals of a later generation tended to accept patristic, especially conciliar, doctrinal formulations as definitive expressions of the truth of a mystery. The original authors of these formulations did not share such delusions. They were seeking to confront and combat errors, not to trap and encapsulate divine mysteries in human formulations.

Thirdly, there was the inclination of some Christians to think through the implications of their faith as fully as possible.

This came to the fore with Clement of Alexandria, and especially with Origen, in the attempt to synthesize Christian truth and Greek wisdom. As one of Origen's disciples expressed it: "He taught us that the river of truth is one." Those currently striving to return to the pristine purity of the original Christian sources often speak of this turn toward a speculative synthesis in terms of a contrast between the Semitic sources and their Hellenistic transformation (or corruption). Such a stark contrast is a bit simplistic. The Hellenistic spirit had a strong influence in the formulation of the New Testament texts themselves. The real point at issue, for them and for us, is the drive to understand as completely as possible the truths already accepted as a matter of faith. This inevitably leads to development in the direction of more precise formulations, more adequate theories, and more searching questions.

Before considering the Council of Chalcedon, the focus of our concern in this section, we shall attempt to indicate how the motives just enumerated gradually modified the answer to the question: Who is Jesus of Nazareth? For the earliest writers, the Trinity (a term Tertullian introduced later) was concretely presented in terms of missions, the sending forth of the Son and the Holy Spirit. In accord with the peculiarly Semitic nominalism characterizing much of the Old Testament, a name was thought to express and somehow embody a personality. 'God' was the Father's name and, as such, could not be the Son's name.

The Gnostics, the most important heretics of the early Christian era, initiated an abstract treatment of the relation of the Son to the Father, relying on a theory of processions that was partially Platonic and partially a residue of Near Eastern mysticism. Their theological aberrations induced many early Fathers to reject such a mode of explanation and to repudiate the use of such abstract non-scriptural terms as 'homoousion' (consubstantial) introduced by the Gnostics. However, such reactions could not long suppress the drive to understand in a deeper way truths accepted on faith.

The naive realism of Tertulian (+ c. 230) illustrates a slightly later stage of this development. In explaining the distinction between the Father and the Son, he placed excessive reliance on images: speaking a word, water from a font, light from the sun. These analogies may have clarified the significance to be accorded to 'the generation of the Son,' but seemed incompatible with the unity of substance between the Father and the Son. Origen (+ c. 254), conditioned by Alexandrian Platonism, purified Trinitarian thought of the materialism inherent in earlier, more imagistic thinking, by insisting on the spirituality of God and the spiritual generation of the Son. The Platonic notion of participation, which he used to explain this generation, carried, as a dissonant overtone, the implication that the Father is superior to the Son. Origen, who was not much of a metaphysician, could not clarify this difficulty. Arius (+ 336) attempted to do so by insisting that the Son is a super-creature, essentially inferior to the Father.

The disputes Arius' teaching occasioned induced the Emperor Constantine to call the first Ecumenical Council at Nicea in 325. The basic purpose of the Council was to present a Creed which would condemn the Arian heresy and serve as a basis for unifying the quarreling bishops. Since no records of the conciliar proceedings have survived—if they ever existed—one must rely on historical reconstructions based on fragmentary sources.[22] However, one crucial point seems clear. It was the Emperor Constantine himself who proposed the acceptance of the key word, 'homoousios' and prodded the bishops into accepting the Creed containing this (as well as other anti-Arian phrases) as the basis of unity. Since acceptance of the statement that the Son is of the same nature as the Father subsequently served as the definitive expression of orthodox beliefs, it is important to consider the precise significance which should be attached to this key term.

'Homoousios' was a manufactured term using 'ousia' as its principal element. The meaning of 'ousia' is somewhat ambiguous in Greek, depending upon the user's philosophical allegiance. Its basic meaning, 'substance,' refers to a particular entity regarded as the subject of qualities. But Aristotle, who made this meaning basic, also used it in a generic sense to connote a universal essence. This latter sense was the meaning the term usually had with Platonists. For the Stoics, 'ousia' simply meant matter. This ambiguity was not removed by coupling this base term to a prefix meaning 'same.' The Gnostics had introduced 'homoousios' into theological discussions as a part of doctrines which were subsequently condemned. Origen used this term to express participation in the same essence. The Arians understood this term in its Stoic or materialistic sense, a sense that they thought had already been condemned. (The condemnation at Antioch of the doctrines of Paul of Samosata in 268 seems to have involved his use of this term.)

This was the term that Constantine (who was not yet a baptized Christian) advocated as the key term for settling the raging dispute. This term was not only unscriptural; it wallowed in ambiguity and reeked of heresy. Constantine carefully qualified his proposal to insist that the term carried no quasi-physical (or materialistic) implications. After considerable debate the assembled bishops eventually accepted this formulation. It seems that they did so, not primarily because of coercion on the emperor's part, but because the term did the job required. It unequivocally condemned Arianism and served as a minimal basis for unity. But it could do this job only if one did not give a precise interpretation to this term, but rather allowed it to be accepted in any Orthodox non-Arian sense. Thus Eusebius and Athanasius were both accepted as Orthodox, though they clearly attached different meanings to this pivotal term.

We will postpone analyzing the epistemological significance to be attached to the affirmation of such a creedal statement until we have discussed the Chalcedonian decree. Here the problem was not the relation of the Son to the Father, but the relation of divinity and humanity in Christ. Again, the significance to be attached to this decree cannot be understood without some historical background.

The school of Alexandria, conditioned by Platonism, Stoicism, and Origen's speculative synthesis of Greek wisdom and Christian doctrine, approached the problem of the unity of Christ by inquiring into the coming to be of the unity of God and man in Jesus. Both Athanasius and Cyril, the two most important Alexandrian theologians, developed a *Logos-sarx* interpretation. The divine *Logos,* the Word of God who rules and orders the cosmos, took on flesh. This, Cyril insisted, was what St. John taught: "The word became flesh." However, 'Logos' for Athanasius had Stoicist overtones which it did not have for John the Evangelist. More importantly, 'sarx' did not mean 'flesh' as a principle distinct from 'spirit' for the original evangelist, as it did for those conditioned by Greek philosophy. In this *Logos-sarx* theology the *Logos* was considered the individuating factor. Accordingly, while this interpretation strongly emphasized the divinity of Christ, it ran the risk of denying that he was truly human.

Antioch, conditioned by Aristotelian philosophy and by centuries of rivalry with Alexandria, developed a rather different Christology. A tradition running from Theodore of Mopsuestia through Nestorius approached the problem of the unity of Christ by asking how the man, Jesus, was assumed by God. This approach certainly preserves the distinctness of the divinity and humanity in Christ. But it made the unity of Christ a third thing to be set opposite the two independent beings, the *Logos* and the man Jesus. Nestorius' explanation of this (or perhaps Cyril's misinterpretation of Nestorius' actual doctrine) was condemned in 431 at the Ecumenical Council in Ephesus which Cyril dominated. This condemnation left the Alexandrian school in the ascendency and, with Dioscorus, St. Cyril's successor as Patriarch of Alexandria, the monophysitism (one nature in Christ) latent in the Alexandrian view became explicit, particularly in the writings of Eutyches.

The reaction against this teaching led to the Council of

Chalcedon (451), the largest and most important of the early Church councils. The concern of the Fathers at this Council was to safeguard what they took to be the authentic Christian tradition against heretical innovations stemming from Hellenistic modes of speculation. To do this they had to find a formula which would express not only the unity of Christ with the distinctness and completeness of both his Godhead and his manhood, but also how this unity and distinctness were to be understood. Here, as earlier at Nicea, scriptural terms proved inadequate as a basis for distinguishing orthodox and heterodox views. The Council's actual text[23] represents a mosaic of phrases drawn from Scripture and the differing theological schools represented. Yet, two non-scriptural terms ('prosopon' and 'phusis') play a pivotal role in expressing the doctrine that Christ is one person with two natures. True God, he is also true man with a rational soul and a human body.

Grillmeier, whose masterful study of Chalcedon we have been adapting, gives the following appraisal:

Here, as in almost no other formula from the early councils, all the important centers of Church life and all the trends of contemporary theology, Rome, Alexandria, Constantinople, and Antioch, have contributed toward the framing of a common expression of faith. . . . The historical significance of Chalcedon is that it tackled this problem . . . with two conceptual distinctions. At first sight this seems a very meager reason for assembling several hundred bishops from all over the world. . . . But these concepts were to become the vessel and expression of the Church's central dogma of the person of Jesus Christ.[24]

The term 'Orthodox' was introduced as a label for those who accepted the truth of the Chalcedonian formulation. The precise wording of this decree was accepted as a standard of orthodoxy not only in Rome and Constantinople; it was also incorporated into the texts of the Augsburg Confession (1530), the Scottish Confession of Faith (1560), the Thirty-Nine Articles of the Church of England (1563), and the Westminster Confession of Faith (1647).[25]

What significance is to be attached to the acceptance of the truth of such a formulation of doctrine as a basis for Christian orthodoxy? In attempting to answer this, I shall first indicate the extreme views that seem to me to be untenable. Some recent critics, notably van Buren[26] and Dewart,[27] have revived Harnack's claim that this decree represents a Hellenization of the Christian message. Just as Scripture does not teach science, so too, it is argued, the councils do not teach metaphysics or philosophical anthropology. If the Hellenistic views on these topics reflected in conciliar decrees are disregarded as outmoded, then we are also free to disregard this particular conception of Christology without rejecting a basic orthodoxy. But if the conceptual distinctions introduced by Chalcedon are simply disregarded as outmoded, then there is no significant way to distinguish between the doctrine the Council affirmed as Orthodox and the one it rejected as heretical.

On the other hand, the Fathers of Chalcedon had no intention of presenting a philosophical explanation, or even a precise definition, of their pivotal concepts. After several decades of theological turmoil generated, in large part, by the differences between Alexandrian and Antiochean doctrinal formulations and the difficulties involved in finding Latin equivalents for technical Greek terms, the Fathers of Chalcedon were as aware as any contemporary analyst that the precise meaning of a term depends on the conceptual framework in which it functions. One cannot, accordingly, accept such formulations as definitive explanations of the problems involved. They were never intended to meet that need.

To get at the significance of 'true' as predicated of creedal affirmations and conciliar decrees, let us develop the parallelism mentioned earlier between the role such theological statements play and the role played by empirical generalizations in scientific explanations. An empirical generalization seeks to express in a unified way a functional relationship found in a multitude of particular instances. It achieves this by the introduction and systematic deployment of technical terms and by an idealization which smooths out the individuating features found in particular instances. Where factual claims have a low-level first-order dependence on a conceptual framework, empirical generalizations are characterized by a functional second-order dependence. Empirical generalizations use a conceptual framework as a vehicle for distinguishing and relating elements, but the emphasis is on the relation expressed rather than on the manner in which the elements are categorized. For this reason the distinguishing truth-feature of such generalizations is their covariance (or form-invariance) under conceptual transformations.

Creedal affirmations and conciliar decrees, such as the two cases considered, rely on the pivotal role which technical, usually non-scriptural, terms play in expressing in a single statement a truth previously fragmented in the varying images, metaphors, parables, and Semitic circumlocutions found in scriptural accounts. Such a unified precise formulation represents an idealization and a smoothing out of the noetic and emotional overtones of the individual scriptural statements. Do the further aspects of this parallel hold, particularly the distinctive second-order dependence on a conceptual framework and the truth-characteristic of covariance under conceptual transformation?

I believe that they do, though in a manner that manifests characteristic differences. Let us begin with the problem of the mode of dependence of the affirmed proposition on a conceptual framework. Here Chalcedon is particularly illuminating because the detailed documentary background on the theological debates and the proceedings of the Council supplies some basis for evaluating the intention of the Fathers involved. As indicated earlier, they recognized the differences between the theological systems and languages characterizing Alexandria, Antioch, and Rome, and had no intention of making any one of these frameworks normative. Hence their mosaic of parallel phrases expressing essentially the same doctrine. They were using conceptual frameworks and technical terms functioning within these frameworks to reaffirm the received doctrine and distinguish it from errors they thought corrosive. Suppose, à la the time machines of science fiction, that we could confront one of these Fathers, explain the presuppositions behind our present questions, and ask him what form of dependence the formulation he endorsed had on a particular conceptual framework? I suspect that he would hold for a first-order dependence inasmuch as they are simply reaffirming traditional doctrine in traditional language, but for a second-order dependence inasmuch as the new critical formulations relied on such technical non-scriptural terms as 'homoousios,' 'prosopon,' 'hupostasis,' and 'phusis.' These terms were reluctantly introduced and grudgingly accepted only because they did the job required. What the Fathers were wedded to was not the precise meaning that might be attributed to these terms, but the role they played in distinguishing orthodoxy from heterodoxy.

It may seem misleading to impose such epistemological ideas as second-order dependence upon a conceptual framework on the long dead Fathers of the early Church. But it would be much more misleading to impose on them a fundamentalist type of literal first-order dependence. All of the theological traditions considered distinguished between literal and varying types of allegorical interpretations of Scripture. The Alexandrian tradition, in particular, stressed the primacy of allegorical interpretations. This means that they accepted scriptural statements as true but substituted new meanings for the literal meanings. If the allegorical meaning is to be related to the literal meanings of the propositions on which it rides, then there must be some covariance across interpretative frameworks.

In developing the idea of covariance with respect to empirical generalizations, we stressed the normative role played by general principles, such as conservation laws. Something analogous obtained with respect to the varying formulations given in patristic theological development. Thus the Christological controversies considered were shaped by an adherence to two overriding principles. The first was quasi-philosophical and insisted that there was no *phusis* without a *hypostasis*. The second was essentially soteriological and stated that what was not assumed was not redeemed. These supplied general guidelines within which the discussions developed.[28]

But there is a more subtle dependence on conceptual frameworks, one that our fictitious Chalcedonian epistemologist would presumably not be aware of. This is the role played by the underlying conceptual background, something which he shared even with the adversaries he was opposing. He would presumably not be aware of this because, for the reasons discussed in the second lecture, no one can distinguish from within a given conceptual framework the precise degree to which he is affirming the conceptualization of reality that undergirds his explicit affirmations. The ontic boundaries of an affirmed proposition are necessarily fuzzy.

However, some degree of clarification comes from comparing their shared conceptualization with our partially different one and relying on our own more developed awareness of the role such conceptualizations play. Using such criteria we can indicate some of the shared presuppositions underlying these conciliar decrees which seem dubious or even wrong today. First, they presumed that what it meant to say that Christ *has* a divine nature, or is of the same substance as the Father, is clear. The only real question in their minds was whether or not it is true. Today we are not at all clear about what it means to speak of someone having a divine nature.[29] This is not so much a question of agnosticism as of the limits of language. Thomas Aquinas represents a later and more developed stage of reflection on this problem: "For we cannot grasp what God is, but only what he is not and how other things are related to him. . . ."[30] Yet Thomas thought that the basic validity of the concepts we employ was determined in a quasi-causal way by the objects from which these concepts were abstracted. With this notion of objectivity he had no reluctance about deducing

from the premise that God is Creator and First Cause the conclusions that God is simple, perfect, good, immutable, eternal,
omniscient, etc. Today the Euclidean rigor of these deductions
looks less than convincing. We cannot express what God is in
himself. Whatever we can express about him is based on our
interpretation of how he is manifested in the world.

Secondly, the Fathers presumed that what it meant to say
that someone has a human nature is quite clear. This is not to
imply that they were affirming any particular *theory* about
human nature. However, they were clearly reflecting the un-
questioned view that what man is can be explained in terms of
a nature plus properties and that this nature is essentially
the same for all men. Neither of these aspects can be considered
unproblematic today. If 'nature' is taken as an ordinary language term, a part of the descriptive metaphysics shared by the
Indo-European languages, then it does not really denote an
ontological principle. As an ordinary language term, its application to differing persons is to be explicated in terms of family
resemblance or, to use Körner's term, the logic of resemblance
classes. This is not necessarily a denial of the objective validity
of the "nature plus property" conceptualization of man. It is
basically a clarification of the way ordinary language terms
function. They do not get their meaning by reference to ontological principles. Though the conciliar Fathers introduced
technical terms, they did so in an ordinary language context.
They, and subsequent Councils, have clearly repudiated reliance on any particular theory. Even if one were to grant the
validity of the term 'nature' as designating an ontological
principle, or in saying that man has a nature, this nature must
now be considered to be conditioned by biological and social
evolution. It is, accordingly, somewhat simplistic to speak of
all men sharing in exactly the same nature.

Thirdly, in speaking of Christ as having two natures which
are unconfused, immutable, indivisible, and inseparable, the
Chalcedonian Fathers spoke as if the two natures were juxtaposed like two pieces in a jigsaw puzzle. Regardless of the

precise significance to be attached to 'nature,' the realities referred to through these terms are so different that they could not be juxtaposed in this way or anything analogous to it.

These are aspects of the underlying conceptualization that are used, but not affirmed. They were neither affirmed nor denied, for their validity was not the question at issue. We who lack their innocence cannot reaffirm their formulations without also consciously affirming one particular view on issues that are now explicit and disputed. Whatever warrant we may have for such affirmations, it does not come from Nicea, Chalcedon or the minimalist interpretation of Church decrees that is an official part of the Catholic tradition.

Finally, even on their own terms, the Councils of Nicea and Chalcedon did not resolve the theological difficulties they treated. Their formulations encapsulated the received tradition and distinguished this from erroneous alternatives. In so doing they indicated the criteria that must be accepted in every Christological theory that lays claim to being orthodox. But such a solution is essentially ecclesiastical and pastoral rather than theological. It is intended to be truth-preserving and order-preserving. It does not show how the two ends of the chain meet somewhere beyond the vision of those who affirmed the existence of such a juncture.[31]

If this underlying conceptualization of man, of God, of sharing, and of theological explanation is presumed rather than affirmed by the conciliar decrees, and if much of it is judged inadequate or untenable, need it be retained by those who wish to retain a basic orthodoxy? A 'No' seems indicated—but the situation is not that simple. These formulations fulfilled a function. One who accepts them as authoritative and binding, yet rejects some of the presumptions and framework features implicit in these formulations, must find a new formulation which fulfills the function the old ones fulfilled. This poses rather stringent requirements for anyone wishing to reconceptualize dogmatic pronouncements. *Intrinsically,* i.e., with respect to the particular doctrine in question, the new formulation must distinguish and relate its constitutive elements in such a way that it can manifest a covariance with the structure of the authoritative but outdated formulation. Such covariance under conceptual transformation is a necessary but not sufficient condition for the acceptability of the new formulation. *Extrinsically,* the new formulation must have a basic consistency with other aspects of the Christian tradition accepted as true. Finally, the ultimate pragmatic norm, the new formulation, must eventually be accepted as valid, though not necessarily as normative, by the community of believers, especially by those possessing doctrinal authority within the community. The degree to which currently proposed reformulations of these Christological doctrines meet these criteria will be considered, at least sketchily, at the conclusion of this lecture.

IV

TRUTH AND THEOLOGICAL THEORIES

It might be wise to begin this new section by giving a summary outline of what was said about the problem of truth in scientific theories. The development of a scientific theory presupposes certain preconditions. The first of these is conceptual. Scientists studying a new domain must discover which descriptive features of the phenomena under observation are particularly useful for grouping and differentiation and then initiate a provisional classification on the basis of such criteria. This initial selection and classification has usually proved to be the most protracted and confused stage in the development of any science. Next, scientists should determine which features, isolated according to one set of criteria, e.g., the atomic chart, are correlated with features isolated according to other useful criteria, e.g., wave lengths of spectral lines. This preliminary step is generally developed through a dialectical interaction of observation, description, correlation, and conceptual analysis.

Ideally it leads to a body of established facts, empirical generalizations, and some guiding principles.

A full-blown theory logically comes after the establishment of such a body of facts and principles. However, since the theories introduced usually begin as creative reorganizations of the conceptualizations employed in cataloging the facts, there is no sharp demarcation between a pretheoretical and a theoretical era. Nevertheless, theories do add a distinct explanatory dimension. How this is accomplished depends on the type of science involved and the currently accepted ideas of what it is to give a theoretical explanation. The type of theories we considered in the previous lecture also involved a dual language system, a physical language and a mathematical language, interrelated by complex correspondence rules.

Building on such considerations plus a more detailed analysis of different types of theoretical statements, we concluded that, while theories may be labeled 'false' when they lead to false conclusions, it is somewhat simplistic to label theories 'true.' Rather than have such an all-or-nothing labeling, it was more helpful to consider the truth status of various types of theoretical propositions such as factual claims alleged to be true on speculative grounds, general principles, and existential claims, and then to examine the role each such statement type plays in the development and acceptance of a theory.

Theological theories exhibit a somewhat similar complexity. As with scientific theories, it is a bit misleading to ask whether a particular theological proposition is true while prescinding from the theoretical framework in which it functions. We must, accordingly, examine the nature, structure, and mode of functioning of theological theories if we wish to investigate what is entailed in accepting propositions embedded in such theories as true—or at least as candidates for this status.

An initial distinction might be made between particular theological theories, concerned with the clarification and explanation of some special point, and general theories, such as

St. Thomas' *Summa Theologiae* or Paul Tillich's *Systematic Theology,* which attempt a systematic integration of theology. Since particular theories usually presuppose general background theories and since only general theories exhibit all the features we wish to consider, we will focus our consideration on them. What I wish to consider in particular is the *Summa Theologiae* of St. Thomas Aquinas. As you have undoubtedly noted by now, I am fascinated by theories and their proper analysis. Except for quantum mechanics, there is no theory which I found more fascinating as an object of study or on which I spent more time than St. Thomas' *Summa.* But my reasons for focusing on this are not simply private ones. This work has played a uniquely privileged role in the development of Catholic thought. This is particularly true of the twentieth century, where the thought of St. Thomas has achieved a quasi-official status due to repeated papal endorsements and has served as the basis for a renewal of Catholic theology and philosophy.

Ideally, the development of theories presupposes an established body of knowledge comprising particular facts and empirical generalizations. It also presupposes a fairly clear idea of what it is to give a theoretical explanation. The Fathers of the Patristic era had neither of these elements in a developed form. But this situation changed in medieval times. The high Scholastic era began with an organization of established facts and principles in theology. It had, in fact, a theological counterpart of the *Handbook of Chemistry and Physics.* This handbook was called *The Sentences of Peter Lombard* and contained in summary form the accepted positions of the Fathers and of some official ecclesiastic pronouncements on most basic points in theology. These *Sentences* played a unique role in the development of theological theories. A budding young theologian would sharpen his theological teeth by lecturing on the *Sentences.* If he was ambitious, he would eventually write a commentary attempting to find or impose a unification on the rather heterogeneous mass Peter supplied.

The second necessary ingredient was a developed idea of

what it is to give a theoretical explanation. St. Thomas accepted the Aristotelian account of scientific explanation and went beyond it in three essential respects to develop his distinctive idea of theology as the supreme science. First, he carried the process of analysis, which his synthesis presupposed, further than Aristotle both in the intrinsic and extrinsic analysis of being. Aristotle's intrinsic analysis resolved beings into the constitutive principles of substance and accident, matter and form. Through his distinction between essence and existence and his distinctive doctrine of the act of existence as the ground for whatever reality a being possesses, Thomas added a newer and deeper level to the intrinsic analysis. Thomas' extrinsic analysis terminated with God as first efficient and ultimate final cause of all being. Though Aristotle's Prime Mover was presented as an ultimate final cause, he was not a first efficient cause and, in fact, did not know the world. Secondly, in presenting his synthesis of theology, developed in accord with the *ordo disciplinae,* Thomas fused the Aristotelian idea of science as an explanation through causes with the neo-Platonic idea of explaining reality through an emanation from and a return to the source of being. Finally, Thomas adapted the Aristotelian idea of subalternation to explain theology as subalternate to revelation. Theology is a science about God and about other things inasmuch as they are related to God. The truths accepted as basic are those God has revealed. These truths, Thomas argued, play a role in theology similar to the role mathematical principles play in physical reasoning.[32]

Our basic concern here is with an evaluation of Thomas' ideas on what a theological explanation is and what it accomplishes. Such an evaluation depends, in a critical way, on the role attributed to true propositions in theological explanation. This cannot be grasped unless one has some understanding of how Thomas' program of systematic theological explanation is actually developed. For this reason I will give a schematic outline of the *Summa,* indicating how the different elements considered were fused into a coherent synthesis.[33]

I. *Pars Prima:* On God.

    A. Nature of Sacred Doctrine (Q. 1)

    B. God (QQ. 2-43)

       His Existence and Essential Attributes (QQ. 2-26)

       As Triune (QQ. 27-43)

    C. Procession of Creatures from God (QQ. 44-119)

       Production of Creatures by God (QQ. 44-46)

       Distinction of Creatures (QQ. 47-102)

          An explanation of what different types of beings, especially angels and men, are in the light of their ultimate extrinsic and intrinsic principles.

    D. Conservation and Governance (QQ. 103-119)

       An explanation of how divine providence works through secondary causes.

II. *Pars Secunda:* Movement of Rational Creatures toward God.

    I-II. General Considerations

    A. God as Man's Ultimate End (QQ. 1-5)

    B. Means of Attaining This End (QQ. 6-114). This is a consideration of human acts considered as leading to or away from beatitude.

       Human Acts in Themselves (QQ. 6-48)

          Concentrates on volition (active) and passion.

       Principles of Human Acts (QQ. 49-114)

       Intrinsic Principles (QQ. 49-89)

          These are habits and virtues. Also treated is sin considered as a turning away from man's last end.

       Extrinsic Principles (QQ. 90-114)

          These are the laws by which man is instructed and the grace by which he is guided.

    II-II. Detailed Consideration of Human Movement Toward God.

A. Virtue, Vices, and Gifts (QQ. 1-170)

This is a detailed, hierarchically-ordered consideration of particular virtues and the acts they govern:
first, the theological virtues, then the cardinal virtues. The correlative vices are also treated. The gifts
of the Holy Spirit are considered as perfecting these
virtues.

B. Specific Conditions Differentiating Men (QQ. 171-89)

Here he treats such charismatic gifts as prophecy
and miracle-working, the difference between the
active and contemplative life, and different offices
and states of life. These are considered and evalu-
ated only with respect to man's ordination toward
God.

III. *Pars Tertia:* Christ as Man's Way toward God.

A. Christ as Savior (QQ. 1-59)

First he treats Christ as the union of God and man,
secondly the properties consequent upon this union,
and finally the theological significance of Christ's
deeds and suffering.

B. The Sacraments Through Which Salvation Is Achieved
(QQ. 60-90, Suppl. QQ. 1-68)

St. Thomas died after completing Q. 90. The supplement was written by his assistant following
Thomas' ordering and utilizing Thomas' earlier
commentary on Peter Lombard's *Sentences.*

C. Resurrection and Eternal Life (Supplement QQ. 59-99)

Before appraising this as theology, it is worthwhile to point
out again what a beautiful piece of work this is as an example
of theory construction. It represented a unified coherent sys-
tematization in accord with fixed principles and an explicit
methodology of all the doctrines St. Thomas considered true
concerning man, his origin and nature, his destiny and the

means that led to or away from his proper end, the world he lived in and the proper interrelation of all essential aspects of this world, as well as all the accepted truths of doctrinal and moral theology. The whole was grounded in God, who was accepted, not as part of the system, but as the ultimate source of all being and intelligibility. No other synthesis developed by the mind of man has had the sweep and structure, the scope and depth, of the *Summa* of St. Thomas.

Yet, one cannot consider this *Summa* today without being acutely aware of some major conceptual dislocations intrinsic to his development. In saying this I am *not* referring to such things as his geocentric view of the universe or the other scientific inadequacies expressed or reflected. As a veritable army of neo-Thomists have shown, these can be changed while the essential features of his synthesis are preserved. What I am referring to is basically St. Thomas' explanation of what theology is. My criticisms here are both epistemological and theological. To get at this I would like to comment on three aspects of the *Summa* which represent, in my opinion, major conceptual dislocations. In each case the difficulty considered is intimately related to the role which St. Thomas assigns to propositions which are *true* in a primary sense and hence serve to ground theological explanation.

First, a doctrine of God's intervention in and transformation of human history has been redeveloped in a way that is essentially ahistorical. That this is so is not surprising. The idea of an historical mode of understanding was not at all clear until writers from Herder through Hegel made it a problematic issue. Yet the idea that revelation was had essentially through the divine ordering of historical events was a fundamental element of the original Judaeo-Christian tradition.[34] Jesus' own preaching was certainly apocalyptic. The question of whether or not he expected an *imminent* parousia, a decisive divine intervention marking the end of the age and a transformation of the human condition, may be debatable. But the conclusion that his preaching was in the late Jewish apocalyptic tradition seems beyond debate. The significance this has as a way of understanding has been rather forcefully brought out by Pannenberg:

A decisive element in this process [of the early Church coming to recognize God in Jesus] was the fact that the conception of reality opened up by the God of the Bible—viz., that reality is *history hastening towards an End*—was raised by apocalypticism to the same universality as lay in the Greek understanding of the cosmos as an ever-stable order. Only in this way could the God of history come into view as the author of all reality in the domain of Greek thinking, at the same time transforming its understanding of the world. . . . Then theology will understand the world as God's world, history as the field of his action, and Jesus as his revelation.[35]

This view of the world as a catastrophically unstable cosmos hurtling toward destruction until rescued through a transforming divine intervention faded in Hellenistic Christianity. Yet, the events related in Scripture were still understood in something of an historical mode. The middle Platonism and neo-Platonism, which most of the Patristic writers reflected, substituted for the timeless Platonic forms a view of reality as emanating from and returning to God and attempting to fit human history, especially salvation history, into this perspective. St. Augustine's monumental *City of God* pictured human history as an arena in which the city of Jerusalem, those who love God in preference to self, fought the city of Babylon, those who love self in preference to God.

For St. Thomas the primary object of faith is the first truth inasmuch as it is divinely- revealed. Divinely revealed truths are known to us through propositions, rather than through historical events. Among systematically interrelated propositions there must be an essentially timeless necessary ordering. Thus, among naturally known propositions, the principle of non-contradiction is primary. Similarly, in the salvific truths known through faith there is a first principle: "Whoever would draw

near to God must believe that he exists and that he rewards
those who seek him" (Heb. 11, 6). Other revealed truths are
related to this in a way that is essentially independent of historical ordering, though implicit principles may *per accidens*
only become explicit in the course of time.[36]

The essentially stable, meticulously ordered cosmos of
Greek rationalism was Thomas' intellectual habitat. Here a
radically historical sequence of events came to be represented
by timelessly true propositions arranged in a sequence that is
essentially logical rather than historical. The biblical word for
truth, *'emeth,'* implied firmness, God's fidelity to his promise
that is gradually unfolding in history.[37] Thomas' *'veritas'* is an
essentially timeless correspondence between a proposition and
that of which it is affirmed. This systematic ahistorical mode
of understanding is legitimate and, for some purposes, even
necessary. Doctrines accepted as true should manifest an internal coherence, and logical analysis can make this explicit.
But such a transformation necessarily involves a drastically
different way of understanding the events which are system-
atized. If the meaning of a proposition is the role it plays in a
conceptual framework, then such a radical transformation of
frameworks necessarily alters the meaning of basic propositions.
This, in turn, alters what is involved in accepting a theological
proposition as true.

The second major conceptual dislocation is the place of
Christology. In Thomas' system it is outside the central schema
of man's emanation from and return to God. The basic reason
for this is clear. In Thomas' thought man is necessarily caused
by and ordered to God, while the Incarnation is not necessary.[38]
It is an accident in the technical sense that it could have been
otherwise. Contingent facts are not entailed by necessary truths
and do not fit into a system bound together by conceptual
entailment.

Twentieth-century Protestant thought, especially the crisis
theology of Karl Barth, witnessed the opposite extreme. God
can be known only through a faith-acceptance of the event of

Jesus Christ as the revelation of God. This is certainly misleading. Jesus himself presumed that his hearers already knew the God of Israel. But it does capture an essential theme of the Christian tradition. The person and life of Jesus is the supreme revelation of God for man. God reveals himself to us primarily through what Jesus was and did. St. Thomas did not exclude this. His theological understanding was conditioned by an ongoing Christian tradition which he fully accepted and lived. But the primacy of Jesus as a revelation of God does not fit into a geometrically ordered deductive system of first truths and entailed propositions. In any such system the distinction between necessary and contingent has a methodological primacy over God's free self-communication in the saving event of Jesus.

Finally, I wish to consider whether St. Thomas' explanation of what theology is really fits what he actually does. Here, I believe, he is somewhat confused. This is not altogether surprising. Many great system builders have given somewhat misleading metasystematic commentaries on what they were doing primarily because of the difficulties involved in taking a detached objective view of one's own brain children. Thus, Newton's occasional remarks on scientific methodology do not really explain what he is doing in the *Principia*. Because of conflicting requirements, which he accepted, St. Thomas felt obligated to reconcile two different views on the basis of theology. The first, stemming from the Aristotelian norm of explanation, insists that the principles of theology, the supreme science, must be true, primary, certain, of the same nature as and causative of the conclusions that flow from them. Secondly, as a Christian who accepted revelation as the highest source of truth, Thomas felt obliged to accept as first principles truths about God which God himself had revealed.

These two views are reconciled through the notion of quasi-subalternation.[39] Subalternation is an idea Aristotle introduced to explain the relation between mathematics and such physical sciences (in his sense of the term) as optics, harmonics, and astronomy, through the idea that the physical science presents the fact while mathematics supplies the reason for the fact. St. Thomas adapted this to theology by distinguishing one science's subordination to another by reason of subject matter and by reason of the way of knowing involved. In theology, as he explains it, the subject matter is God. The first principles are those truths about God which man could not naturally know, but which he comes to know because God reveals them. These are the articles of faith which virtually contain the subject matter of theology.[40]

If this program were actually followed, then the systematic development of Thomas' theological synthesis would flow from propositions which he accepts as true on the grounds that they are revealed. But do articles of faith really play this role in the *Summa?* As the schematic outline indicates, the first premise in the deductive synthesis is the proposition that God exists and that he is the first cause and last end of all things. But is this something known by *faith* or *reason?*

St. Thomas used both terms in a technical sense and insisted that what was known by reason could not also be known by the same person by faith. Though what is in itself knowable by reason might be known to some individual only by faith, e.g., because of intellectual limitations, nevertheless anything knowable by reason cannot be an *article* of faith.[41] By reason one can know both that God, the Creator, exists and that he is man's last end. Therefore it would seem that the fundamental premise grounding Thomas' theological synthesis is derived from reason rather than revelation

St. Thomas would undoubtedly answer this objection with a crucial distinction. The bare fact may be knowable by reason but the way in which it is understood is dependent upon revelation. Through reason one can know *that* God is but cannot know *what* God is in any positive sense. God, however, does comprehend himself and can communicate an expression of this self-knowledge geared to a limited human way of understanding. He has in fact done this by revealing that he is, that he created the world in time without reliance on any pre-existent matter, and that he will be an object of direct knowledge to the blessed in heaven, i.e., he will take the place of the impressed intelligible species in an intrinsically timeless act of knowing which cannot have an expressed species, or a concept.

Does Scripture really teach such doctrines? Devout scientists, seduced by Gifford lectureships, are not the only ones who practice concordism, reading 'the truths of science' back into Scripture. St. Thomas clearly did something similar in projecting 'the truths of philosophy' back into Scripture. The rationale he employed was clear. Sacred Scripture conveys first principles by means of metaphors.[42] This is particularly true of the *Pentateuch* because Moses, whom St. Thomas accepted as the author of these books, was speaking to a rude people. What the theologian must do is to get at the truth taught by means of the metaphor.

By following this principle, St. Thomas can uncover the first truths taught by Scripture. When God told Moses: "I am who I am" (Ex. 3, 14) he was revealing that he is a pure act in whom existence and essence are identical.[43] The most basic feature distinguishing God from creatures, accordingly, is that only God is a subsistent existence and that everything apart from God participates in existence.[44] For this reason God is first, final, and exemplary cause of all things.[45] Moses himself did not present things quite this way, but "it should be considered that Moses was speaking to a rude people and in order to condescend to the weakness of their minds he only proposed things apparent to the senses."[46] The implication is clear. Moses himself understood the realities he was discussing through their constitutive principles (i.e., he thought as a Thomist). Then he *translated* his ideas into a metaphorical terminology intelligible to a rude nomadic tribe. Thus when Moses speaks of the original earth as being without form and void (Gen. 1, 2), he did not mean a complete lack of form. But he spoke this way because his audience did not understand the difference between primary and signate matter.[47] For the same reason he did not explain the work of distinction in terms of the four elements and the correct views of time and space.[48] When Thomas in turn substituted intelligible for sensible language, he was not projecting philosophical doctrines into Scripture. He was simply recovering the pristine truth rather than its simplified popularization.

Both this manner of interpreting Scripture and the spirit of concordism it manifests are unacceptable. Articles of faith, i.e., doctrines that cannot be established by pure reason and which are accepted as true exclusively because they are believed to have been revealed, do not play the role in St. Thomas' theological synthesis that he attributes to them. Only once, in fact, does Thomas really hold a pivotal truth exclusively because it is an article of faith. Through reason he can demonstrate that the world was created, but not that it was created *in time*. He holds the latter only because it is an article of faith.[49]

This is not to imply that the *Summa Theologiae* is essentially a work of philosophy rather than theology. It clearly is not. But its real unity comes, not from the role Thomas attributes to revealed truths as first principles for a quasi-deductive process, but to his idea that theology, the science of the divine, should imitate the way of knowing proper to God. The primary object of God's knowledge is God himself. In knowing himself and his free act of creation he also knows creatures as causally dependent upon him. If the theologian strives to first know God and then to know creatures in terms of their dependence upon God, his manner of knowing resembles the divine self-knowledge on which theology is ultimately based. This is what Thomas attempted to do. His somewhat misleading meta-systematic remarks are conditioned by his acceptance of the Aristotelian doctrine that explanation is essentially deduction from first truths and by his concordist interpretation of Scripture.

If a doctrine of truth does not play the role in theological explanation, even in Thomistic theology, that St. Thomas attributes to it, what role does it play? Rather than attempt a global answer to this, let us return to the problem that supplies a connecting link in these differing theological periods, the question of how the relation between man and God in Jesus is to be understood. Let us also consider how the acceptance of certain doctrines as true conditioned Thomas' treatment of this problem.

The *Sentences* of Peter Lombard listed three different views on the meaning to be attached to the propositions "God is man" and "God becomes man." The relation of the divine and the human in Christ was understood in terms of: the *assumption* of a man by the divinity, the *subsistence* of a composite explained by the existence of a divine person in both a divine and human form, and a *body-soul composite,* which is neither a person nor a substance, which the Person of the Word takes on as a garment.[50]

The early attempts to decide between these views relied almost exclusively on logic and dialectics. St. Thomas brought two new features to this discussion. First, he attempted a metaphysical rather than a purely logical explanation. Secondly, he seems to have been the first medieval theologian to have read the decrees of the Council of Chalcedon.[51] This decree, as he interpreted it, taught the subsistence view as the true doctrine. In this case the theologian's task is not so much to decide what is true but to come to a more adequate and unified understanding of a doctrine already accepted as true.

The new understanding came from Thomas' metaphysical doctrine of existence as an act distinct from essence. If being a person is fundamentally a way of existing, i.e., if the act of existence is the ultimate personalizing factor, then the fact that Christ is one person implies that he has only one act of existence and that this act is divine rather than human. He is a divine person. Since nature, or essence, is really distinct from existence, a human nature, distinct from the divine nature, can participate in or be actuated by a communication of a divine act of existence.[52] Though Christ's human nature does not have its proper act of existence but has instead a finite participation in an infinite act, this does not imply any deficiency in Christ's human nature. Since essence, or nature, is distinct from existence, the particular mode in which existence is communicated to an essence does not affect its perfection as a principle of being. Thomas could say, accordingly, that Christ was true God and true man, perfect in his divinity and perfect in his humanity without any mingling or confusion of the natures.

The distinctive metaphysical underpinning given this doctrine, accepted as true, allowed for an integrated understanding of other doctrines also accepted as true on authoritative grounds. Thus Thomas could use his distinctive doctrine on the composition of Christ to relate the divine and human components in Christ's knowledge, to explain his actions as being truly human and yet having a salvific efficacy, and to explain his mode of being present in the Church and through the sacraments.

In discussing the relation between theories and empirical generalizations in science, we attempted to bring out their differing status with respect to the acceptance of propositions as true. Empirical generalizations are accepted as true basically on inductive grounds, rather than because they are deduced from propositions accepted as true. A theory does not prove that these propositions are true. Its role is to supply an intelligible integration of a collection of laws by explaining why the laws are obeyed, by correcting their limitations, and by extending their significance to further domains. The fact that a theory accomplishes this does not prove that the theory is true. It is, in fact, somewhat simplistic to apply 'true' to theories *tout court*. However, it is sometimes possible to isolate characteristic propositions of the theory and accept these as 'true.' This happens especially when a theoretical proposition can, in principle, be detached from a particular theory and be shared by otherwise competing theories.

I believe that something similar obtains in the case of theological theories, at least for the type of theories we are now considering. The orthodox theological theorist accepts certain doctrinal formulations as true and seeks for a new and more unified understanding of their significance. The fact that a theory successfully accomplishes this result does not guarantee the truth of the theory. Even if one were to accept the key doctrines as true, e.g., the real distinction between essence and existence and the conception of existence as first act, this acceptance is essentially philosophical rather than theological.

Yet doctrines, even philosophical doctrines, introduced as parts of theological theories may come to be accepted as theological truths. This happens when a doctrine may be so detached from a particular theory that it may be shown to be a necessary ingredient in any theory that seeks to explain the doctrine in question. Thus any explanation of the accepted theological doctrine on sin necessarily presupposes a doctrine of free will. Such propositions are the ones that Catholic theologians have traditionally designated by the theological note "theologically certain."[53] I believe that such propositions are often neither theological nor certain—even granted the truth of the theological propositions they are introduced to explain. What this note really means is that if certain accepted theological propositions, derived from Scripture or tradition, are understood in a certain way, then this mode of understanding entails the acceptance of other propositions. Particular theories, e.g., medieval Scholastic theories, share a common conceptual framework. Propositions radicated in such shared frameworks and traditionally listed as "theologically certain" are in many cases more an explication of background features and implicit presuppositions of the conceptual framework than they are the enunciation of implicitly revealed doctrines.

The chief reason for bringing this up is the fact that many current developments in theology either call into question or simply reject the conceptual framework and set of shared presuppositions that undergirded previous theological explanations. This, in turn, entails rejecting many doctrines traditionally accepted as theologically certain. This need not mean a rejection of orthodoxy. It could mean a redefinition of 'theologically certain' in terms of non-revealed doctrines that must be accepted as true in *any* framework in which doctrines, accepted as true because revealed, can receive an intelligible formulation. Such a consideration of the possibility of radically redeveloping theology brings us rather precipitously from the thirteenth to the twentieth century.

IV

The Radical Renewal of Theology

Seven centuries is a long leap. Yet an inclusion of the theological developments of this period would not contribute substantially to the particular problematic we are considering—what it means to say that a theological proposition is true. Thus, the Reformation and Counter-Reformation eras witnessed, to be sure, many investigations into the truth of theological propositions and the implications of accepting or rejecting such truths. But these investigations tended to be more inquisitorial than analytic. In the Enlightenment era the emphasis gradually shifted from Catholic-Protestant polemics to theology-science apologetic confrontations. The nineteenth century witnessed the nadir of Catholic theology and some developments in Protestant theology which reached their culmination in the twentieth century. And with this brief background we will leap from the mid-thirteenth to the mid-twentieth century.

The problematic of truth takes various forms in contemporary theology. For our purposes we can make an initial distinction between tradition-guided theology and radical theology. This distinction is crude and somewhat simplistic, but it does allow us to focus on the problem we wish to consider. By 'tradition-guided theology' I refer to the work of theologians who accept the preceding traditions as a source of truth and explicitly build a theology on this basis. This would include the neo-orthodoxy of Karl Barth and the neo-Thomism of Karl

Rahner and Bernard Lonergan. These may well be the most important developments in twentieth-century theology. But the predication of 'true' in such contexts does not present *epistemological* problems very different from those already considered in treating scriptural statements, conciliar decrees, and theological propositions based on a utilization of these sources.

By 'radical theology' we are referring to developments which explicitly break with the preceding traditions and seek to reinterpret the significance of Christianity. Such a theology presents a new and rather interesting problem concerning the implication of 'true' as predicated of theological propositions. It allows, indeed demands, an exploration of the rather fuzzy border separating the reinterpretation of Christianity from the effective abandonment of Christianity. Instead of speaking of *a* border, it would be a bit more accurate to speak of three successively lower boundary limits. The highest and strictest level is set by those who possess the authority to determine what must be accepted as a condition for full membership in a particular sect. The next lower level is doctrinal rather than authoritarian and comes from the acceptance of a core of propositions as a minimal standard for orthodoxy. The lowest boundary, and one of a rather different nature, is epistemological. Implicit in the idea of accepting Christianity is the acceptance of Christian teaching as true in a normative sense. Such an acceptance, of itself, does not specify which propositions are true. But without some such acceptance in principle, Christianity has effectively become an inspiring story rather than inspired doctrine. With the rise of radical theology comes the delicate distinction between a reinterpretation, which accepts Christianity as true in this normative sense, and a reinterpretation which effectively rejects this.

Rudolf Bultmann is the central figure in these developments. His program of demythologizing is so well known that another summary, even a brief one, may well bore anyone familiar with contemporary theology. However, we have many non-theologians here and some sort of summary is necessary if we wish to come to grips with the *epistemological* problems implicit in Bultmann's theological program.[54]

The New Testament, as Bultmann interprets it, reflects a mythological view of the cosmos and of man. The cosmos is pictured as a three-story affair with God and his angels in the top story, man in the middle, and Satan and his demons on the bottom. Both angels and devils can make excursions into the world of man, can control human actions and influence human history. The world of man, corrupted by Satan, can be saved from imminent catastrophe only by the decisive intervention of God. Accordingly, in the fullness of time God sent forth his Son, a pre-existent divine being, who appeared on earth as a man by being born of a virgin. On the cross he who lived without sin died the death of a sinner to atone for the sins of man and turn away God's wrath. His resurrection from the dead is a personal triumph over Death, the demonic forces of sin and evil which have held man in bondage since the sin of Adam. The risen Christ is exalted to the right hand of God in heaven and made Lord and King. His resurrection and exaltation prefigure the coming triumph of his followers when he will come again on the clouds of heaven to preside over the general judgment of all men and to abolish sin, suffering, and death. Though the precise time of this eschatological event is uncertain, the young St. Paul reflected the common view that it would happen soon, probably within his own lifetime.

This mythical view of man and his cosmos, a view which Bultmann attributes to a fusion of Jewish eschatology and pagan Gnosticism, is judged unacceptable, indeed unintelligible, to a modern man. A local heaven and hell find no place in a scientific view of the cosmos, nor does a doctrine of miraculous intervention by celestial and infernal beings accord with the scientific ideal of natural explanation. Man's understanding of himself has also changed. One cannot now accept a view of man in which human actions are explained through the supernatural interference of superhuman beings. Any doctrine of man as a being responsible for his own actions and their consequences undercuts the idea that the death of a sinless man could somehow atone for the guilt of others or that an ultimate triumph is had through the resuscitation, transformation, and exaltation of a corpse. With this conception of Jesus as redeemer gone, there is no reason for believing in his personal divinity or his pre-existence.

This mythology must go. But the question is: How is it to be disposed of? Simply dropping the mythical elements while retaining the non-mythical residue leaves a few bland generalities deprived of any real theological significance: "The question is whether the New Testament message consists exclusively of mythology, or whether it actually demands the elimination of myth if it is to be understood as it is meant to be."[55] Hence his program of first demythologizing Scripture and then reinterpreting it in language that is meaningful to contemporary man. This, for Bultmann, is essentially the language and thought of Martin Heidegger. Thus, the doctrine that the world of man is essentially corrupted by sin is reinterpreted as the view that man is so beset by anxiety about objects that he cannot achieve authentic existence. Using the historical Jesus as an inspiration, one may derive from the New Testament a picture of Christ as a truly authentic man, one whose example invites others to imitate the self-commitment through which man's original possibility of a truly authentic existence may be achieved.

Because of his central role in contemporary theology, Bultmann's position has been extensively criticized.[56] I will focus on his epistemology, rather than his theology, and especially on what he has contributed toward a clarification of the role truth-claims play in theology. Here, I believe, Bultmann made a decisive contribution in coming to grips with the problem that was tending to undermine the neo-orthodox Protestant tradition. Since Scripture presents God's truth, it must, it was felt, stand in judgment over man. As Karl Barth expressed it: "The Church is apostolic and therefore Catholic when it exists on the basis of Scripture and in conformity with it, i.e., in the orienta-

tion which it accepts when it looks only in the direction indicated by the witness which speaks to it in Scripture, with no
glances aside at any other direction."[57] Yet the progress of
Scripture studies was forcing man to stand in judgment over
Scripture. Before accepting the teaching of Scripture, one had
to judge what it is that the Scriptures actually teach. Any such
interpretative judgment necessarily relies on our culturally
conditioned ideas of what is acceptable.

Barth's unique—and uniquely untenable—solution to the
noetic problems involved was to fashion an epistemology in
accord with the norms supplied by the Lutheran doctrine of
justification by faith alone. Just as God can choose a man as
his agent totally independent of any worth that man (a worth-
less sinner by nature) might possess, so he can also choose and
justify words independently of their intrinsic suitability (always
zero) to express God. Scripture communicates knowledge about
God, not because of the meaning of the language used—all
language is equally useless in this regard—but because it is God
who is using it. Barth's theology may be a soul-stirring procla-
mation of God for the contemporary world but, as Evans has
shown,[58] Barth's second-order commentary on his own procla-
mation is radically unintelligible.

Bultmann's program offers a way out of this epistemological
impasse. Acceptance of the teaching of Scripture as true, far
from obviating the need for judgment, makes critical judgment
a necessity. To be accepted as true, the message of Scripture
must be understood. To be understood, Scripture, like any set
of documents, must be given an interpretation that distinguishes
the central teaching which has an abiding significance from the
accidental features which reflect the limitations of a past era.
Unfortunately, Bultmann's mode of demythologizing and reinterpretation has an almost one-dimensional simplicity that
distorts some of the basic issues. The language of Scripture
reflects a view of the world and of man's place in it. Bultmann
attributes this to mythological thinking. But *any* language
necessarily reflects a view of the world and of man's place in it,

a view that is conditioned by a cultural history. Scripture begins with a demythologized version of the creation accounts common in the ancient Near East, and the subsequent pages show an abiding concern with the problem of demythologizing. Nor does mythological thinking play that crucial a role in the New Testament.

Rather than a simple program of stripping off elements considered mythological and rewriting the message in Heideggerian language—a language that strikes many Anglo-Saxon philosophers as being more mythological than anything found in the New Testament—one should think in terms of the various conceptual levels previously considered and the role they play in supplying a vehicle for the New Testament teaching. Acceptance of this teaching as true entails acceptance of a *covariance* between scriptural propositions and our own formulations. But our formulations, to be acceptable, cannot be had by the simple substitution of Heideggerian for New Testament mythology. Our reformulations must reflect our view of the world and of man and our more sophisticated view of the role of language.

In spite of these and other shortcomings of execution, Bultmann's program of reinterpreting is, in my opinion, essentially correct. Accordingly, what we wish to consider is the sort of reinterpretations that have subsequently been developed and the status accorded basic truth claims in these redevelopments. To make this even sharper we will focus on the question that has been central in this lecture: Who is Jesus of Nazareth?

As a preliminary, we should note the decisive significance attached to the doctrine of Christ's divinity by two of the most influential theologians in the history of Christianity. St. Thomas, a man never given to overstatements, said: "If therefore the human nature is not united to the Word of God in a person, it is not united to it in any way. And thus faith in the Incarnation is totally removed, which is to destroy the whole Christian faith."[59] Martin Luther also insisted that the denial of this doctrine is the destruction of Christianity: "This is the

chief doctrine of the Christian faith. . . . Hence those who deny
the divinity of Christ lose all Christianity and become Gentiles
and Turks through and through."[60] There has been an unin-
terrupted tradition stretching from the Christological controversies in the early Church to the recent decision of the Unitar-
ian Church to drop "Christian" from its name, a tradition
insisting that any rejection of the proposition that Christ is
divine is a rejection of Christianity. Thus, the World Council
of Churches, at its New Delhi meeting, issued a declaration that
strongly affirmed the centrality of this doctrine: "The World
Council of Churches is a fellowship of churches which confess
the Lord Jesus Christ as God and Saviour according to the
Scriptures. . . ."

Earlier we spoke of an epistemological lower limit setting
minimal standards in determining what constitutes an acceptance of Christian teaching as true. The doctrine that Christ
is divine is certainly such a limiting proposition. But epistemological considerations are not enough to determine the
interpretation to be accorded this doctrine. Recent reinterpretations of Christianity have introduced positions on this point
which are quite at variance with the Chalcedonian interpretation. Some of the writers in question would accept as true the
proposition that Christ is divine, but would not interpret this
statement in terms of two natures coming together in one
person. We may briefly consider some representative views.

Wolfhart Pannenberg, whose theology represents an alternative rather than a sequel to the Bultmannian tradition, insists
upon the divinity of Christ, but thinks of Jesus' union with
God as something that is gradually realized and not properly
understood, even by Jesus himself, prior to the resurrection.[61]
Pannenberg develops this doctrine in such a way that he carefully and consciously maintains a continuity with tradition and
even with the principal Patristic formulations.

Another theologian who is acutely conscious of the problem
(though not the terminology) of covariance under conceptual

transformation is Paul van Buren.[62] Jesus, in van Buren's interpretation, was a singularly free man. His freedom is contagious and sets free those who see his example in the discernment situation that comes with the acceptance of an Easter "blik" (or perspective). Like Bultmann, van Buren attempts to make Christianity meaningful to modern secular man by rewriting Christian doctrine in accord with the norms set by a particular philosophical tradition. However, van Buren opts for analysis rather than Heideggerian phenomenology and effectively accepts as normative some fragments from the rather superficial dialogue previously mentioned concerning the meaningfulness of religious language. Van Buren's secular interpretation of the Gospel, in my opinion, crosses the epistemological border separating the reinterpretation and the effective rejection of Christianity.

Various other reinterpretations have been proposed.[63] For Matthews, Christ is a moving pattern of experience.[64] That is, in speaking of his divinity, one is speaking of his mode of acting rather than his mode of being. Dorothea Sölle accepts the *cultural* validity of the claim that God is dead and attempts to present an interpretation of Christ that is intelligible against this background.[65] Christ emerges as the *representative,* the man who temporarily represents God to man and other men before God.

The reinterpretations of Christology so far considered have all been of Protestant origin. Catholicism, so it seemed, was immune to such radical revision thanks to a protective barrier of doctrinal authority. But Pope John opened a door and no one has succeeded in preventing this opening to a changing world from constantly growing. On the North American scene, Leslie Dewart has been the most prominent Catholic to call for a radical renewal of accepted theological formulations. I wrote a criticism of his views which caused a certain amount of misunderstanding.[66] I should state clearly that though I found some fault with the way in which he developed his views, I believe that what he is trying to do is correct. I have, in fact, little hesitancy in accepting him as a charismatic figure riding the wave of the future.

However, the really radical Catholics in this area are certainly the Dutch theologians. A. Hulsbosch's article on Christology has precipitated an extensive discussion of this problem.[67] His basic idea is that the divinity of Christ is manifested in the perfection of his humanity. He is God by being man in a special way. In the past, the God-man composition in the person of Christ was explained by analogy with the body-soul composition in man. As such dualistic views of man begin to look increasingly untenable, the explanatory basis for the analogy implicit in the whole Chalcedonian tradition is dissolved. One must return to the original sources which teach that Jesus was *known* to be a man and *believed* to be God, but which never explain the relation between the divine and human in the man Jesus.

Are any such radical reinterpretations of this thesis, so central to the whole Christian tradition, acceptable? This question must ultimately be answered by those who have to make the basic commitment, whether they are individual Christians deciding for themselves, or authoritative Christians making decisions within the limits of their doctrinal and ecclesiastical competence. My concern here is with a second-order question about the implications of predicating 'true' of theological propositions embedded in changing conceptual frameworks and subject to acceptance on the part of an on-going community. How can we allow for the possibility that these radical restatements of Christian doctrine could be accepted as extensions rather than as denials of a basic Christian orthodoxy?

My answer to this question is a rather qualified one depending on the analyses already given of what was accepted as true in the past. We may begin with Scripture and the contemporary stress on revelation as *economic,* in the Greek sense of this term. What is revealed is the basis requisite for the acceptance and living of the faith. Thus God is revealed, not as an *en-soi,* but as a *pour nous.* We do not directly learn what God is in himself, but only how he has appeared for us. The Scriptures do not

even bring us back to the historical Jesus, though events in his
life supply the foundation for the Christ of history presented in
Scripture. Scripture definitely teaches the divinity of Christ—
in him dwelt the fullness of the Godhead corporeally—but
leaves open the manner in which this is to be interpreted.

Subsequent theological developments present a more complex problem. The proposition that Christ is God is at the inner
core of a conceptual system—or overlapping set of conceptual
systems—and serves as a support for other propositions concerning sin and salvation, death and immortality, the essence of the
Church and its sacramental life, and freedom and moral authority. If predicating 'true' of "Christ is divine" implies that this
proposition must manifest covariance under conceptual transformations, then one must consider how these interrelated
theological doctrines may be redeveloped before deciding on
the acceptability of redevelopments in the principal doctrine.

It seems clear, however, that most of these related doctrines
are so beset by criticisms and difficulties that their continued
acceptability will be influenced by critical examination and,
when necessary, radical redevelopment. It is rather easy to list
some of the doctrines which contemporary Christians find difficult to understand and to accept in their traditional sense. Such
a list would include: original sin, conceived as a transgression
by one couple and affecting all their descendants; divine favor-
itism, manifested through the election of one people and the
exclusion of others; reconciliation for sin through the death of
a sinless man; a dualistic view of man with a concomitant doctrine of divine intervention in the formation of a soul; personal
immortality with the binary option of eternal bliss or perpetual
damnation; an eschatological completion of the human world;
revelation considered as a source of truth and infallibility considered as a guardian of truth.

From the point of view of conceptual analysis, these difficulties are all radicated in a framework in which Christian
teaching was given an ontological interpretation. It is currently
fashionable to insist that reliance on metaphysics must go. But

the solution is not that simple. Any language which can serve as a basis for communication necessarily reflects and utilizes a view of the world and man's place in it. It is this implicit ontology, rather than a developed system of metaphysics, that requires critical examination. We cannot simply dispense with this without reducing ourselves to silence. But by making it more explicit we can examine its role in giving shape to the propositions we accept as true and attempt to determine what this acceptance would mean in either a gradually changing or a radically altered conceptual framework.

The shape the doctrines just mentioned will assume in the future cannot now be clearly foreseen. I strongly suspect that the changes we have experienced since Vatican II are relatively minor compared to those yet to come. Yet here, as in the development of science, true progress preserves and even makes manifest the invariance that is present at a deep structural level.

*   *   *

Perhaps after four lectures on 'true' we may conclude by saying something about truth. 'Truth' can be taken as an abstract way of referring to true propositions. But there is also a deeper meaning, as when one speaks of science as the search for truth or of theology as based on revealed truth. 'Truth' in this sense connotes something transcendent: the created universe, which science seeks to fathom through the systematic deployment of a network of theories representing successive approximations to specialized aspects of the universe; the God of creation, whose self-revelation inspires theologians to create linguistic analogs expressing a human understanding of what he is. This transcendent reality is the ultimate ground and goal of the search for truth. But it is a ground which can only be explicated and a goal which can only be approximated by the slow piecemeal process of presenting propositions which we take to be true and hope to be not too inadequate.

The abiding temptation here is to absolutize the relative,

to accept particular propositions as adequate expressions of ultimate truth. This is a temptation especially experienced by those with a passion for the ultimate. Scientists in the Newtonian tradition thought that their physics represented the bedrock reality of the material universe and that future developments would be confined to the fourth and fifth decimal places.

Many philosophers currently manifest a more subtle form of this abiding temptation, this peculiar fate of human reason to struggle with questions which cannot be ignored, because prescribed by the very nature of reason itself, but which cannot be given a once and for all answer because the ultimates sought transcend the limited and relative means available to express them. Currently influential solutions to this Kantian dilemma could fit under the loose label of 'eschatological metaphysics.' The strategy would be something like the following. All our valid and potentially explanatory knowledge about the world is contained, at least in principle, in the natural sciences. Here, however, one must not limit 'science' to formal structures, but rather think of it as a concern of a community of inquirers who use many means of knowing reality, some of which (e.g., deep structures of tacit knowledge) may be opaque to formalization. Science, so conceived, is an on-going concern subject to conceptual revolutions and systematic reformulations. Accordingly, what is ultimate in reality is revealed, not in present science, but, to use Pierce's term, in the eventual consensus of a community of inquirers.

Fortunately, the metaphysician need not wait supinely for this philosophical parousia. He can and should determine which aspects of our cognitional structures will persevere unto the end, and then may use this determination to outline the most basic features of ultimate reality. For Pierce himself, as well as for such other philosophers as G. Bergmann, the abiding features are the laws of logic. For others, like Quine and Sellars, it is the ability of first-order sentential calculus to serve as a vehicle for the rational reconstruction of whatever system is accepted as ultimate. The ontic commitments proper to such

a system must be along the general lines developed in the
Tractatus. For Lonergan, the abiding feature linking present
partial knowledge with the fuller understanding of the far
future is not the laws of logic, but the invariant structure of
all human knowing, a structure that allows an argument by
isomorphism from the composition of the knowing to the composition of the known.

I share with such men an abiding commitment to the quest
for the absolute and the realization that deep structures play a
more basic role in this search than overt propositions. But I
find their particular systems inadequate, though I have not yet
developed something more adequate.[68] This leaves me in a
position similar to Polanyi, with no link necessarily relating the
present to the philosophical parousia except the passionate
commitment to the search for an ever deeper and truer understanding shared by members of an on-going intellectual community. Inadequate and frustrating as this may be, I find it
preferable to suffering the premature hardening of the categories that comes from accepting a metaphysical, or any other,
system as something not subject to future revision.

The attempt to express ultimate reality and absolute moral
standards in theological propositions has been conditioned
more by first-order polemics than by second-order structuralism.
Such precise formulations as creedal affirmations and conciliar
decrees were not formulated as instruments for freezing theological development, but as solutions to pressing controversies.
To accept them as true does not entail making their formulations and the conceptualization undergirding them timeless
absolutes. Such absolutistic pretensions are, in fact, an obstacle
in the search for truth. Here it is helpful to contrast the rigidity
characteristic of older theological textbooks with the flexibility
of formulations found in Scripture. I like to remember that
Ecclesiastes, the Preacher, is also part of Scripture. One of his
basic purposes is to deflate any pretensions of trapping a transcendental absolute in the quicksilver of human speaking and
living.

FOOTNOTES

CHAPTER I

[1] Aristotle, *Posterior Analytics*, I, ii,71b19-22 (Mure's translation), in *The Basic Works of Aristotle*, ed. R. McKeon (New York: Random House, 1941), p. 112.

[2] "As in Mathematics, so in Natural Philosophy, the Investigation of difficult Things by the method of Analysis, ought ever to precede the Method of Composition. This Analysis consists in making Experiments and Observations, and in drawing general Conclusions from them by Induction. For Hypotheses are not to be regarded in Experimental Philosophy. ... This is the method of Analysis: and the Synthesis consists in assuming the Causes discovered, and established as Principles, and by them explaining the Phaenomena proceeding from them, and providing the Explanations." *Opticks*, based on the 4th ed. 1730 (New York: Dover, 1952), pp. 404-05.

[3] Newton's own statement is: "But hitherto I have not been able to discover the cause of those properties of gravity from phaenomena, and I frame no hypotheses for whatever is not deduced from the phaenomena is to be called an hypothesis; and hypotheses, whether metaphysical or physical, whether of occult qualities or mechanical, have no place in experimental philosophy. In this philosophy particular propositions are inferred from the phaenomena, and afterwards rendered general by induction." *Principia Mathematica*, trans. Motte-Cajori (Berkeley: Univ. of California Press, 1962), p. 547.

[4] This is discussed in Melbourne G. Evans, "Newton and the Cause of Gravity," *The American Journal of Physics*, 26 (1958), 619-24.

[5] For summaries of the views of Mach, Poincaré, and Duhem coupled to substantial excerpts from their writings, see Joseph J. Kockelmans, *Philosophy of Science: The Historical Background* (New York: The Free Press, 1968).

[6] Each of these positions is discussed in detail in S. Körner, *The Philosophy of Mathematics: An Introduction* (New York: Harper pb. ed., 1962).

[7] For the early development of logical positivism, see Victor Kraft, *The Vienna Circle*, trans. A. Pap (New York: Philosophical Library, 1953) and Joergen Joergensen, *The Development of Logical Empiricism* (Chicago: Univ. of Chicago Press, 1951). The official statement of the purpose of the Vienna Circle, drawn up by Carnap, Hahn, and Neurath, may be found in Joergensen, pp. 3-5.

⁸ A simple account of the decline and demise of the verificationist theory of meaning may be found in John Hospers, *An Introduction to Philosophical Analysis* (2nd ed; Englewood Cliffs, N. J.: Prentice-Hall, 1967), Chap. IV. A brief but informative summary coupled to a detailed bibliographical essay on these developments may be found in P. Edwards and A. Pap, *A Modern Introduction to Philosophy: Readings from Classical and Contemporary Sources* (rev. ed.; Glencoe, Ill.: Free Press, 1965), pp. 756-60.

⁹ The idea of ontic commitments of formal systems comes from W. V. O. Quine. See his article, "On What There Is," in *From a Logical Point of View* (Cambridge, Mass.: Harvard Univ. Press, 1953). My own usage of the term 'ontic commitments,' however, will not be quite the same as Quine's, but will be more in accord with ideas developed by Wilfred Sellars, especially in his articles "The Language of Theories" and "Grammar and Existence" (both reproduced in his *Science, Perception and Reality* [New York: Humanities Press, 1963]). If one has a theory accepted as explanatory which includes statements of the form (Ex) (Nx), where 'N' is one of the common noun category terms basic to the system, then it is reasonable to correlate such formulas with existence claims.

¹⁰ R. Carnap, "Empiricism, Semantics, and Ontology," included as an appendix in his *Meaning and Necessity* (rev. ed.; Chicago: Univ. of Chicago Press, 1956), pp. 205-21.

¹¹ Ernest Nagel, *The Structure of Science: Problems in the Logic of Scientific Explanation* (New York: Harcourt, Brace & World, 1961), Chaps. V and VI.

¹² A brief survey of this development may be found in my "The New Materialism," *The Heythrop Journal*, VII (1967), 5-26.

¹³ For a general survey of these positions see A. C. Ewing, *The Fundamental Questions of Philosophy* (London: Routledge & Kegan Paul Ltd., 1951), Chap. III.

¹⁴ William James, *The Meaning of Truth: A Sequel to "Pragmatism"* (New York: Longmans, Green & Co., 1909). See esp. the Preface and Chaps. VIII and IX.

→ ¹⁵ J. L. Austin, "Truth," in *Truth*, ed. George Pitcher (Englewood Cliffs: Prentice Hall, 1964), p. 18.

¹⁶ Pitcher, *op. cit.*, pp. 16-17, contains Ramsey's original presentation and, pp. 32-53, Strawson's elaboration, as well as further articles on Strawson's position.

¹⁷ J. Austin in Pitcher, *op cit.*, pp. 18-31.

¹⁸ P. T. Geach, "Assertion," *The Philosophical Review*, LXXIV (1965), 449-65.

¹⁹ Gertrude Ezorsky, "Truth in Context," *Journal of Philosophy*, LX (1963).

CHAPTER II

¹ Heidegger's views on truth will be treated in more detail in the appendix to this chapter.

² To be more precise, "circle" is probably first learned as a descriptive

term characterizing a certain class of shapes. After learning geometry one comes to accept the geometric definition as normative, i.e., in judging whether or not a shape is truly circular.

[3] His arguments against the acceptance of propositions may be found in W. V. O. Quine, *Word and Object* (Cambridge, Mass.: M. I. T. Press, 1960), Chap. VI. For a general survey of the problem and opposing views, see Richard M. Gale, "Propositions, Judgments, Sentences and Statements," in *The Encyclopedia of Philosophy*, Vol. 6, pp. 494-505.

[4] Sellers' treatment of propositions may be found in his *Science and Metaphysics: Variations on Kantian Themes* (New York: Humanities Press, 1968), Chap. IV. For a further discussion on this work see my article-length review in *The Philosophical Forum*, I (1969), 509-45.

[5] James W. Cornman, *Metaphysics, Reference, and Language* (New Haven: Yale Univ. Press, 1966).

[6] Claude Levi-Strauss, *The Savage Mind*, trans. G. Weidenfeld and Nicolson Ltd. (Chicago: Univ. of Chicago Press, 1966).

[7] Bernard Lonergan, S. J., *Insight* (New York: Philosophical Library, 1957), pp. 556-57.

[8] A. J. Austin, "Truth," in Pitcher, *op. cit.*, pp. 18-31.

[9] P. Strawson in Pitcher, *op. cit.*, p. 33.

[10] Aristotle, *Metaph.* IV c. 7, 1011b25.

[11] This analogy was suggested by Michael Dummett in Pitcher, *op. cit.*, pp. 93-111.

[12] W. V. O. Quine, *Methods of Logic* (rev. ed.: New York: Holt, Rinehart and Winston, 1959), p. xii.

[13] P. F. Strawson, *Individuals: An Essay in Descriptive Metaphysics* (Doubleday pb. ed. 1963), esp. Chaps. I and III.

[14] This idea is taken from Stephan Körner, *Experience and Theory: An Essay in the Philosophy of Science* (New York: Humanities Press, 1966). In my extended discussion of this work in *The Review of Metaphysics*, XXII (1968), 125-37, I indicated an acceptance of Körner's contention that resemblance class predicates require a three-valued logic. Since writing that article I have come to accept the criticism of Dharmemdra Kumar in *British Journal For the Philosophy of Science* 18 (1967), 211-22, that indeterminateness in the applicability of such terms is a question of semantics rather than a property of their logic.

[15] Strawson, in Pitcher, *op. cit.*, p. 84.

[16] R. Carnap, "Empiricism, Semantics, and Ontology," in *Meaning and Necessity* (rev. ed.; Chicago: Univ. of Chicago Press, 1956), pp. 205-21.

[17] A preliminary treatment of this relation between speaking about linguistic categories and mental acts may be found in my "Science and Metaphysics: A Critical Review," *The Philosophical Forum*, I (1969), 509-45.

APPENDIX TO CHAPTER II

[1] St. Thomas' most complete treatment of philosophical methodology is contained in his commentary, *In Librum Boetii de Trinitate*, esp. qq. 5 and 6, and in the introductory sections to his commentaries on Aris-

totle's *Physics* and *Metaphysics*. Some discussions which I found helpful
are: James C. Doig, "Aquinas on Metaphysical Method," *Philosophical
Studies*, XIII (1964), 20-36; Thomas C. O'Brien. *Metaphysics and the
Existence of God: A Reflection on the Question of God's Existence in
Contemporary Thomistic Metaphysics* (Washington, D. C.: The Thomist
Press, 1960); and James Reichmann, S. J., "Logic and the Method of
Metaphysics," *The Thomist*, 29, (1965), 341-95.

2 Thomas treats this in *In Librum Boeth. de Trin*, q. 5, a. 3. For a
discussion of this point, see L. B. Geiger, O. P., "Abstraction et separation
d'apres s. Thomas. In de Trinitate, q. 5, a. 3," *Revue des sciences philo-
sophiques et theologiques*, XLVIII (1948), 328-39.

3 Doig, *op. cit.*, p. 31.

4 Thomas' famous five ways of demonstrating God's existence, *Summa
Theologiae*, I, q. 2, a. 3, are quite misleading even as a guide to St.
Thomas' own views on this problem. The *Summa* was written as a theological work in which Thomas presupposed the existence and knowability
of God (cf. q. 1) and the idea that Scripture taught that God's existence
could be known by natural reason. Accordingly, he gave a schematic outline of the traditional ways of doing this. But a philosopher, following
Thomas' ideas on philosophical methology, should not approach metaphysics with the intention of trying to prove God's existence. The operative intention should be a desire to understand the beings of experience.
One concludes to a transcendent source of being and intelligibility only
if finite beings are not intelligible on any other basis. For a further
discussion of this, see O'Brien, *op. cit.* One could almost summarize the
approach Thomas' principles (though not his practice) indicate by saying
that the philosophical theist is a disillusioned agnostic.

5 St. Thomas Aquinas, *De Veritate*, q. 1. a. 1. This has been translated
in a three-volume English edition entitled *Truth* by R. Mulligan, S.J., J.
McGlynn, S.J., and R. Schmitt, S.J. (Chicago: H. Regnery, 1952.) For a
redevelopment of the Thomistic view of truth which stresses the linguistic
and especially the social aspects of truth, see Robert Harvenek, S.J., "The
Community of Truth," *International Philosophical Quarterly*, 7 (1967),
68-85.

6 *Ibid*, q. 1. a. 4.

7 This use of 'truth' presupposes a distinction between logical and
ontological truth. 'Logical truth' in this terminology means the conformity of mind to reality, or what is said to what is. 'Ontological truth'
means the conformity of reality to mind. Thus a true triangle is one that
conforms to our definition of a triangle. In a more ultimate sense, ontological truth was thought of as the conformity of things to the divine
mind.

8 *Summa Theologiae*, I, q. 13, a. 12, c.

9 St. Thomas, "De propositionibus modalibus," 5, 16. The quote is
from I. Bochenski (who edited the critical edition of this work), *A History of Formal Logic*, trans. I. Thomas (Notre Dame: Univ. of Notre
Dame Press, 1961), p. 183.

10 See R. J. Henle, S.J., "Saint Thomas' Methodology in the Treatment
of 'Positiones,'" *Gregorianum*, XXXVI (1955), 391-409.

11 Aristotle, *On Interpretation*, Chap. 1 (16a4-8), *op. cit.* p. 40. We

have used Edghill's translation rather than the new translation by Ackrill, which speaks of 'affections' rather than 'concepts,' because the older version is closer to the type of interpretation available to Aquinas. For Aquinas' commentary on this, see Jean T. Osterle, *Aristotle: On Interpretation, Commentary by St. Thomas and Cajetan* (Milwaukee: Marquette Univ. Press, 1962). In Lesson II (pp. 23-28), Thomas teaches that words primarily signify concepts and that simple concepts—which are determined by objects—are the same for all and do not admit of error.

[12] Ludwig Wittgenstein, *Philosophical Investigations,* trans. G. E. M. Anscombe (Oxford: Blackwell's, 1953).

[13] For a discussion of the development of the doctrine of meaning, see Gilbert Ryle, "The Theory of Meaning," in C. A. Mace (ed.), *British Philosophy in the Mid Century* (London: 1957), pp. 239-64.

[14] I have developed these ideas in a bit more detail in "The Transcendental Turn: Necessary But Not Sufficient," *Continuum* VI (1968), 225-31. However, this essay represents heuristic anticipations of a future program rather than an already developed doctrine.

[15] Heidegger's most explicit treatment of this problem is in his essay, "On the Essence of Truth," trans. R. Hull and A. Crick, in W. Brook (ed.), *Existence and Being* (Chicago: Regnery, 1949). In summarizing Heidegger's views on the problem of truth, I am relying heavily on W. B. Macomber, *The Anatomy of Disillusion: Martin Heidegger's Notion of Truth* (Evanston: Northwestern Univ. Press, 1967) and also on William Richardson, S.J., *Heidegger: Through Phenomenology to Thought* (2nd. ed.; The Hague: M. Nijhoff, 1967). For my limited purposes it is not necessary to take a stand on the question of whether the historical development of Heidegger's thought manifests a fundamental continuity (Macomber) or a definite change (Richardson) in focus from *Dasein* to being between the writing of *Being and Time* and "On the Essence of Truth."

[16] After saying that the fundamental question of philosophy, questioning the meaning of being, must be treated phenomenologically, Heidegger adds: "The expression 'phenomenology' signifies primarily a *methodological conception.* This expression does not characterize the *what* of the objects of philosophical research as subject-matter, but rather the *how* of that research. The more genuinely a methodological concept is worked out and the more comprehensively it determines the principles on which a science is to be conducted, all the more primordially is it rooted in the way we come to terms with the things themselves, . . .": in *Being and Time,* trans. J. Macquarrie and E. Robinson (London: SCM Press, 1962), p. 50.

[17] "On the Essence of Truth," *op, cit.,* p. 337.

[18] *Ibid.,* p. 336.

[19] *Being and Time,* p. 76.

[20] For a discussion of this, see W. Richardson, S.J., "Heidegger and the Origin of Language," *International Philosophical Quarterly,* II (1962), 404-16. The basic idea presented here is that Being-as-*Logos* is at once aboriginal Truth, Ground and Utterance. *Dasein* is the focusing point through which *Logos* comes to pass as Truth, Ground, Utterance. Since being in its truth is aboriginal utterance, we may determine the sense of Being-as-Truth by interrogating language. In spite of the rather strange

and strained terminology, Heidegger's conclusion that a study of being should involve the questioning of language is one that could easily be accepted on other grounds.

[21] *Being and Time,* p. 272.

CHAPTER III

[1] Pierre Duhem, *The Aim and Structure of Physical Theory,* trans. P. Wiener (Princeton: Princeton Univ. Press, 1954), p. 19.

[2] "Epistemological Problems," *op. cit.,* esp. pp. 113-24.

[3] Hanson's most important work in his *Patterns of Discovery* (Cambridge, Eng.: Cambridge Univ. Press, 1958). A complete list of his writings may be found in the recent issue of *Boston Studies in the Philosophy of Science,* Vol. III, dedicated to his memory.

[4] T. Kuhn, *The Structure of Scientific Revolutions* (Chicago: Univ. of Chicago Press, 1965).

[5] S. Jaki, *The Relevance of Physics* (Chicago: Univ. of Chicago Press, 1966).

[6] Stephen Toulmin, "Conceptual Revolutions in Science," in R. Cohen and M. Wartofsky (eds.), *Boston Studies in the Philosophy of Science,* III, 331-47.

[7] My article, "Ontic Commitments on Quantum Mechanics," will be published in *Boston Studies in the Philosophy of Science,* Vol. VI. The philosophical problems involved in the question of scientific realism are discussed in the article-length introduction to my *Philosophical Problems of Scientific Realism* (New York: Appleton-Century-Crofts, forthcoming).

[8] One way to construct such a language would be to number all the cards as follows (using "C" for clubs, etc.) : 1-2C, 2-2D, 3-2H, 4-2S, 5-3C, 6-3D, ... 36-10S. For honors use hundreds: 101-JC, 102-JD, ... 201-QC, ..., 301-KC, ..., 401-AC, ..., 404-AS. This provides a unique specification for each card. Adopting the convention that there are four kinds of numbers (which could be designated by different colors), viz., those in the series: $(4n)$ or hundreds ending in 4; $(4n-1)$ or hundreds ending in 3; $(4n-2)$ or hundreds ending in 2; and $(4n-3)$ or hundreds ending in 1, reproduces the functional equivalent of suits. This language accordingly, can play the role of GL.

To take over the role of SL one should first assign additional values: a void is 300, a singleton is 200, and a doubleton is 100. Since the new deck now totals 4,718 points, compared with the 40 honor points in the Goren SL, one could simply scale the old rules (e.g., open with 1,500 points and a good four card series) and reply "One no series" with 700-1,100 points, etc. This scaling would simply be a first approximation to an adequate SL rule system. Since the new point system is more comprehensive and more revealing than the old, it would undoubtdly be possible to develop a set of SL rules more complex and more informative than anything now available. This system could work—but its acceptance would probably ruin the game of bridge.

[9] "Ontic Commitments of Quantum Mechanics," *op. cit.*

[10] Piaget's ideas are developed in a series of publications extending

from 1923 to the present. The books which have the closest bearing on the present discussion are: *The Growth of Logical Thinking in the Child* (New York: Basic Books, 1958) and (in collaboration with B. Inhelder) *The Early Growth of Logic in the Child* (Norton pb. ed., 1969). The best summary of his views is by John Flavell, *The Development Psychology of Jean Piaget* (New York: Van Nostrand, 1963). When behavorism dominated American psychology, Piaget's views were generally rejected. Recently, he seems to be winning a rather wide acceptance in the psychological views of J. Bruner, G. Miller, and others, while some psychologists, e.g., Berlyne, Werner and Kaplan, put an even greater stress on formal structures in cognitive development than Piaget.

[11] By first-order properties I mean properties of objects, whereas second-order properties are properties of properties of objects. In this sense, even a two-placed predicate, such as a relation, could be a first-order property.

After developing these ideas in the lecture that was given, I came across an independent but quite similar treatment of the relation between ordinary knowledge and formal systems in physics. See the appendix, "Physics and Perception," in David Bohm, *The Special Theory of Relativity* (New York: W. A. Benjamin, 1965), pp. 185-230. Earlier, Max Born had developed somewhat similar ideas, though not in so detailed a way, in his *Natural Philosophy of Cause and Chance* (Oxford: Clarendon Press, 1949), esp. Chap. IX.

[12] For a summary of these developments coupled to an evaluative bibliography, see Marx Wartofsky, *Conceptual Foundations of Scientific Thought* (New York: Macmillan, 1968), Appendix 1. The differences between Descartes' and Newton's theories of collisions are treated in detail in Richard Blackwell, *Discovery in the Physical Sciences* (Notre Dame, Ind.: Univ. of Notre Dame Press, 1969), Chap. I.

[13] Neils Bohr wrote and spoke on this from 1927 till his death in 1962. His clearest presentation is "Discussion with Einstein on Epistemological Problems in Atomic Physics," in *Albert Einstein, Philosopher-Scientist* (New York: Harper pb. ed., 1959), pp. 201-41. For an excellent summary which is probably clearer than Bohr's own accounts of his position, see Aage Peterson, "The Philosophy of Neils Bohr," *Bulletin of the Atomic Scientists,* 9 (Sept. 1963), 8-14. One of the most penetrating critics of Bohr's views has recently come to the conclusion that Bohr's views are superior to anything offered by his critics. See Paul Feyerabend, "On a Recent Critique of Complementarity," *Philosophy of Science,* 35 (1968), 309-31; 36 (1969), 82-105. For Heisenberg's views, see his *Physics and Philosophy: The Revolution in Modern Science* (New York: Harper, 1958) and Patrick Heelan, S.J., *Quantum Mechanics and Objectivity: A Study of the Physical Philosophy of Werner Heisenberg* (The Hague: M. Nijhoff, 1965). The best explanation of the technical problems which led to the devlopment of the Copenhagen interpretation is Max Jammer, *The Conceptual Development of Quantum Mechanics* (New York: McGraw-Hill, 1966).

[14] Some of these possibilities are developed in detail by Stephan Körner in *Experience and Theory: An Essay in the Philosophy of Science* (New York: Humanities Press, 1966), Chap. I. Whether these schemata could serve as the underlying conceptualization of an ordinary spoken

language is debatable. But they could certainly function as conceptual schemata used for empirical differentiation, i.e., as part of a revisionary rather than a descriptive metaphysics.

[15] Newton's conceptualization of physical reality is effectively summarized in the "Definitions" which precede his axioms in the *Principia* (pp. 1-12 in the Cajori edition). This summarizes the use of terms as they actually function in the *Principia,* while his better known *General Scholion,* appended to the second edition, is an attempt to answer some philosophical and theological objections and goes beyond what is in Newton's physics. The mechanistic world-view that developed could not really be explicitated until it came under fire and critics could distinguish between the physical reality that the system was treating and the *conceptualization* of this physical reality implicit in the system. One of the earliest critics, J. B. Stallo, defined the mechanical view of the universe by means of the following theses: (1) the primary elements of all natural phenomena, and, therefore, the ultimates of scientific analysis, are mass and motion; (2) mass and motion are disparate (mass is indifferent to motion which may be imparted to it "from the outside"); (3) both mass and motion are constant. Combining this mechanism with atomism led to four further theses: (1) the elementary units of mass are simple and in all respects equal; (2) they are absolutely hard and inelastic; (3) they are absolutely inert and passive; (4) all potential energy is in reality kinetic energy. It was this sort of philosophical atomism which generated the opposition to the development of scientific atomism. Stallo's views were developed in *The Concepts and Theories of Modern Physics,* first published in 1882 and recently edited and republished by Percy Bridgman. My summary account is based on Joseph Kockelmanns, *Philosophy of Science: The Historical Background* (New York: Free Press, 1968), pp. 147-69.

[16] The first stage is in Book I, sect. XII of the *Principia,* the second stage in Book III, props. vii and viii.

[17] E. P. Wigner, *Symmetries and Reflections* (Bloomington: Indiana University Press, 1967), Chaps. I-II.

[18] P. A. M. Dirac, *Quantum Mechanics* (4th ed; Oxford: Clarendon Press, 1958), p. 15.

[19] From a technical point of view, context-dependent properties are those corresponding to operators that do not commute with all the operators representing conserved quantities. This was established by H. Araki and M. Yanasi in *The Physical Review,* 120 (1960), 622-26. The numerical conclusions given in this paper were corrected by Yanasi in *The Physical Review,* 123 (1961), 666-68. The peculiar logical problems involved in context-dependent predication are discussed by P. Heelan, S.J. in "The Logic of Quantum Mechanics Does Not Have To Be Non-Classical," *Boston Studies in the Philosophy of Science* (to be published).

[20] This may sound like a perversion of the doctrine of induction. But in the cases of concern it is the practice of scientists. The specific conductivity of silver, the spectrum of a rare earth element, the magnetic moment of a particle: such things are determined by a careful examination of a few—often just one—pure samples. The problems and paradoxes which philosophers have raised concerning induction and confirmation generally reflect presuppositions different from those operative in scientific

practice—e.g., the idea of natural types (all protons are the same) is rejected, though it is clearly operative in scientific practice while the truth-functional logic that equates "All ravens are black" and "All non-black things are non-ravens" is treated as if it were the basis for scientific reasoning. For a further discussion of the differences between scientific practice and philosophical reconstructions, see George Schlesinger, "Natural Kinds," *Boston Studies in the Philosophy of Science,* III, 108-22.

[21] Particles are grouped into multiplets having the same spin and parity quantum numbers. Hypercharge is defined as twice the average charge of such a multiplet. Thus the average charge of the neutron (0 charge) and the proton (e^+) is ($\frac{1}{2}$)e^+. Baryon quantum numbers are assigned: $+1$ for baryons (protons, neutrons, and other heavy particles), -1 for anti-baryons; 0 for kaons, mesons, leptons and their anti-particles. Then the strangeness quantum number of a particle is defined as the hypercharge minus the baryon quantum number.

[22] For a discussion of different functioning levels as a consequence of energy thresholds, see V. Weisskopf, *Knowledge and Wonder* (Anchor pb., 1966).

[23] Ernest Nagel, *The Structure of Science* (New York: Harcourt, Brace & World, 1961), Chap. V. In Nagel's account, the distinction between laws and theories is explained in terms of the type of sharp theoretical-observational dichotomy that we have rejected. However, the general validity of Nagel's distinction between experimental laws and theories does not depend on the acceptability of the interpretation of science in terms of a theoretical language and an observational language. On this point see Henry C. Byerly, "Discussion: Professor Nagel on the Cognitive Status of Scientific Theories," *Philosophy of Science,* 35 (1958), 412-23.

[24] This is a slight oversimplification of the history involved. Lavoissier first thought of oxygen as the acid-making principle. Priestly and Cavendish in England showed that hydrogen and oxygen combine to form water, but they interpreted these experiments in terms of the phlogiston theory and the idea that air and water are both simple elements. Lavoissier repeated their experiments and was the first to give a correct interpretation. The only point that has any bearing on the present discussion is that, before the development of atomic physics, 'oxygen' was necessarily defined in terms of the gross properties oxygen gas displays.

[25] Isaiah Berlin adapted a Greek fable about hedgehogs and foxes to introduce the analogy of the analyst who is like a hedgehog in that, though he just focuses on one thing, he endeavors to see it clearly. Scientists have recently clarified the reason for the hedgehog's sharply limited interests. Its neocortex, the brain development distinguishing higher animals, is about the least developed of any mammal. See I. T. Diamond and W. C. Hall, "Evolution of Neocortex," in *Science* 164 (Apr. 18, 1969), 251-61. One likes to believe that the sharply limited interests of many analysts can be explained on some other basis.

[26] Newton himself actually rejected the view of action at a distance and refused to give a causal explanation of gravity. However, action at a distance was the position implicit in the coupling of his mathematical treatment and the idea that there is an absolute void between heavenly bodies. This idea was made explicit in Cotes' preface to the second edition

of the *Principia* and accepted by most subsequent scientists until Faraday rejected it.

[27] A product of a covariant and a contravariant vector summed over all four coordinates is covariant with respect to Lorentz transformations. By writing all equations in this form, e.g., in the formula for the conservation of energy and momentum, $P^\mu P_\mu = m^2 C^2$, relativistic quantum mechanics is developed in such a way that the requirement of covariance is automatically fulfilled.

[28] Claude Levi-Strauss, *The Savage Mind, ed. cit.; Totemism,* trans. Rodney Needham (Boston Press, 1962); *Le cru et le cuit, Mythologiques* (Paris: Libraire Plon, 1964). His explanation of the role of structures in human thinking, whether primitive or scientific, fits quite well with the emphasis I have been according higher order predication and covariance in the expression of thought. Thus, when a primitive tribe is divided into exogamous moieties the distinct subgroups are usually given names derived from plants and animals. Such totemism has been widely practiced by primitive groups that have had no interconnection in historic times, e.g., Amerindinians and Australian tribes.

As long as anthropologists attempted to explain this in terms of the logic of first-order predication (I am a bear while you are a crow implies that I am strong and you are sly), they were unable to develop an adequate explanation of totemism.

In Levi-Strauss' analysis, what is basic is not a mystic identification of man and animals, though this may be an eventual consequence, but the solution of an epistemological problem. Members of the tribe are known as individuals and identified by names, while animals and plants are known as members of a group and identified by class names. Until a culture develops to the point where it can abstract the idea of a class from instances, the only means conceptually available for dividing a tribe into subgroups is the concrete classificatory schemes already functioning. This totemic classificatory schema supplies a vehicle for linguistic differentiation only if the *systematic* character of each domain is brought to the fore. This means that the basic analogy is not between natural species and social groups but between the differences: species: species::group: group.

Nature: Species 1 + Species 2 + Species 3 + ... + Species n
Correspondence ⬍   ⬍   ⬍   ⬍
Culture: Group 1 + Group 2 + Group 3 + ... + Group n

First-order predication is concerned with putting individuals into groups; second-order predication with interrelating the groups.

His study of mythology leads to a similar emphasis. Traditional attempts to interpret myths focused on the details of the myth and their historical or allegorical significance. Levi-Strauss concentrated on the transformations myths undergo in passing from one culture to another or through their continued retelling in a preliterate culture. While the details change, their interrelation manifests a structural invariance, which implies that the details must manifest a basic covariance. In Levi-Strauss' interpretation, this is because the human mind works through grasping associated pairs and a binary opposition. When the original binary opposition proves inadequate to express the phenomenon in question, one transforms to a different conceptualization which goes beyond the original binary pair in allowing a middle term.

Thus, the Zuni myths of origin and emergence are concerned with coming to grips with the mysteries of life and death. Since this pair admits no middle term, one gets mythic equivalents that do.

Initial Pair	First Triad	Second Triad
Life	Agriculture	Herbivorous animals
	Hunting	Carrion-eating animals
Death	Warfare	Beasts of prey

The chart indicates his analysis of the transformation of myths. Agriculture supports life and does not involve death; warfare causes death but does not support life. Hunting is intermediate in that it both involves death and supports life. The second triad can be given a similar interpretation. When the story of Romeo and Juliet served to structure *West Side Story, West Side Story,* in turn, could serve to give a new and deeper significance to a new film production of *Romeo and Juliet.*

This correspondence, however, does not imply unconditional support for his ideas on the srtucture of the human mind, ideas which are ultimately based on the phonemic analysis of the Prague school.

[29] This has effectively been done by P. Achinstein in terms of the question: What does it mean to say that someone has a theory? See his *Concepts of Science: A Philosophical Analysis* (Baltimore: The Johns Hopkins Press, 1968), Chap. IV.

[30] "Epistemological Problems in the Philosophy of Science," *The Review of Metaphysics,* XXII (1968), 113-37, 329-58, esp. 113-24. For further developments of this point see Achinstein, *op. cit.,* and N. R. Hanson, "Logical Positivism and the Interpretation of Scientific Theories" (to be published) .

[31] See Otto Redlich, "Thermodynamics since Caratheodory," *Reviews of Modern Physics,* 40 (1968) , 556-63.

[32] Laslo Tisza, "The Conceptual Structure of Physics," *Reviews of Modern Physics,* 35 (1963) , 151-85.

[33] N. R. Hanson, *Patterns of Discovery, ed. cit.,* Chap. V.

[34] Karl Popper, *The Logic of Scientific Discovery* (New York: Science Editions, Inc., pb., 1961) and his collection of essays, *Conjectures and Refutations* (London: Routledge and Kegan Paul, 1963) .

[35] It might seem that one of the most influential works in contemporary philosophy of science is at variance with this. C. G. Hempel and P. Oppenheim in "Studies in the Logic of Explanation," *Philosophy of Science,* 15 (1948) , 135-78, give four rules for the logic of explanation. The fourth, the empirical condition of adequacy, is that the sentences constituting the explanans (the deductive base) must be true. These four requirements have served as a basis for most discussions of the logic of scientific explanation. The contradiction, however, is more apparent than real. What these two authors were interested in working out was analogous to a truth table for scientific inference. Working out the logical structure of truth tables does not determine which factual propositions are true. Accordingly, they defined "law" in such a way that every law is true—if it is not true it is not a law. But, as Hempel's own analysis of the paradoxes of confir-

mation made clear, statements found in the different sciences could not be known with certainty to be true. They should be classified as 'law-like statements' rather than laws. Then the Hempel-Oppenheim logical analysis effectively says: If these candidates for the status are accepted as laws, then certain conclusions follow.

36 "Ontic Commitments of Quantum Mechanics," *op. cit.* Formula (1) is an adaptation of a formula developed by S. Körner.

37 This is especially true in Quine's writings, and is one of the reasons why my use of 'ontic commitments' is closer to Sellars' explanation than to Quine's. See footnote 9 of Chap. I.

38 The papers by F. Reines and C. Cowan summarizing their final results and analyzing the problems connected with an experimental determination of the neutrino's collision cross-section may be found in *The Physical Review*, 113 (1959), 273-78, 280-86. The account of the meeting is based on my memory of it, which is quite fallible on such details as names, dates, and places.

39 This history and its philosophical implications are summarized in N. R. Hanson's *The Concept of the Positron* (Cambridge, Eng.: Cambridge Univ. Press, 1963).

40 The paper by Bilaniuk and Sudarshan is in *Physics Today*, 22 (May, 1969), 43-51. Gell-Mann introduced 'chimeron' in *Proceedings of the XIIIth International Conference on High-Energy Physics* (Berkeley: Univ. of California Press, 1967), pp. 3-9. My evaluation of the status of other theoretical entities derives chiefly from a reading of articles in *Physical Review Letters*.

41 Tachyons come out as ontic commitments of the special theory of relativity only if this theory is supplemented by the Gell-Mann totalitarian principle which states, somewhat facetiously, that in physics anything that is not prohibited is compulsory. This could be considered a reformulation of Leibniz's principle of sufficient reason.

CHAPTER IV

1 Edward MacKinnon, S.J., "Linguistic Analysis and the Transcendence of God," *Proceedings of the Catholic Theological Society of America*, 23 (1968), 28-44.

2 John Wisdom's article, "Gods," reproduced in various anthologies, e.g., in A. Flew, *Logic and Language*, I (Oxford: Basil Blackwell, 1951), initiated the contemporary discussion of the cognitive character of religious language. For further stages of the discussion see A. Flew and A. C. MacIntyre, *New Essays in Philosophical Theology* (London: Student Christian Movement Press, 1955); John Hick (ed.), *The Existence of God* (New York: Macmillan pb., 1964); and Anthony Flew, *God and Philosophy* (New York: Harcourt, Brace and World, 1966). For defenses of theological statements as significant, though not cognitively meaningful, see: R. B. Braithwaite, *An Empiricist's View of the Nature of Religious Belief* (Cambridge, England: Cambridge University Press, 1955); T. R. Miles, *Religion and the Scientific Outlook* (London: George Allen and Unwin, Ltd., 1959); Paul van Buren, *The Secular Meaning of the Gospel* (New York: Macmillan pb., 1966).

[3] This is a position which, I believe, would be held by most philosophers of science, whether theists, atheists, or simply undecided. Thus E. Nagel writes: "The versions of the verifiability theory commonly used to show that theism has no cognitive meaning also exclude most scientific theories (e.g., theories about the atomic constitution of matter) as meaningless, and are unacceptable for at least this reason. More generally, I do not find the claim credible that all theistic statements are meaningless nonsense, and I believe that on the contrary theism can be construed as a doctrine which is either true or false and which must therefore be assessed in the light of the arguments advanced for it." This is from his article, "A Defense of Atheism," in P. Edwards and A. Pap, *A Modern Introduction to Philosophy* (New York: The Free Press, rev. ed., 1965), p. 462. Similar views are presented in the articles by N. R. Hanson and P. Feyerabend in the symposium on atheism presented in *Continuum*, V (1967), pp. 5-117. In Hanson's case this represented a repudiation of the view developed earlier in "On the Impossibility of Any Future Metaphysics," *Philosophical Studies*, 11 (1960), 86-96, which would dismiss theism as meaningless. His final position was that theism, though false, was cognitively meaningful.

[4] The significance of this point is particularly clear when one considers radically different religious traditions. Evans-Pritchard could clarify the Zande use of 'Mbori,' roughly analogous to our 'Supreme Being,' only by showing how the use of this term fits into different aspects of the natives' life. See E. E. Evans-Pritchard, "Zande Theology," in his *Social Anthropology and Other Essays* (New York: The Free Press, 1962), pp. 288-329.

[5] John Herman Randall, Jr., *The Role of Knowledge in Western Religion* (Boston: Star King Press, 1958), p. 15.

[6] St. Cyril, Epist. 40 ad Acad., quoted from Johannes Quasten, *Patrology*, Vol. III (Utrecht: Spectrum, 1960), p. 140.

[7] This text from Chalcedon is quoted from Aloys Grillmeier, S.J., *Christ in Christian Tradition: From the Apostolic Age to Chalcedon (451)*, trans. J. S. Bowden (New York: Sheed and Ward, 1965), p. 481.

[8] *Summa Theologiae*, III, q. 2, a. 2, c.

[9] Leslie Dewart, *The Future of Belief: Theism in a World Come of Age* (New York: Herder and Herder, 1966), p. 150.

[10] Pope Paul VI, "The Credo of the People of God," reproduced in *The Pope Speaks*, 13 (1968), 273-82. The quotation is from p. 277.

[11] This quote is given in the article by Robert North, "Recent Christology and Theological Method," *Continuum*, VII (1969), 63-77. The quote is on p. 66.

[12] Thus, in his recent encyclical, *Mystery of Faith*, Pope Paul discussed the authoritative and unchanging status proper to the formulas given by the Ecumenical Councils, particularly the Council of Trent. The reason given for this unchangeableness is: "For these formulas, like the others which the Church uses to propose the dogmas of faith, express concepts which are not tied to a certain form of human culture, not to a specific phase of human culture, nor to one or other theological school. No, these formulas present that part of reality which necessary and universal experience permits the human mind to grasp and to manifest with apt and

exact terms taken either from common or polished language. For this reason, these formulas are adapted to men of all times and all places." For a commentary on the theological significance to be accorded this theory of language, see "Dogma, Freedom, Change, and Continuity," in *Herder Correspondence,* Vol. 5, #9 (Sept. 1968), 265-70.

13 For a discussion of this phrase and its changing significance, see Herbert Vorgrimler, "The Significance of Christ's Descent into Hell," trans. T. L. Westow, in *Concilium: Theology in an Age of Renewal* (New York: Paulist Press, 1966), Vol. 11, pp. 147-59. It may be helpful to list some recent works on the problem of the development of doctrine which have shaped the views presented here: Karl Rahner, "Considerations on the Development of Dogma," in his *Theological Investigations,* Vol. 4 (New York: Helicon Press, 1966), pp. 1-30; Henri Rondet, "Do Dogmas Change?" *Twentieth Century Encyclopedia of Catholicism,* Vol. 5 (New York: Hawthorne Books, 1961), pp. 7-120; Edward Schillebeeckx, O.P., "Exegesis, Dogmatics and the Development of Dogma," in *Dogmatic vs. Biblical Theology,* ed. H. Vorgrimler (Baltimore: Helicon, 1964), pp. 115-45; J. H. Walgrave, "Development of Dogma," *New Catholic Encyclopedia,* Vol. 4, pp. 940-44; and especially the two recent studies by Avery Dulles, S.J., "Dogma as an Ecumenical Problem," *Theological Studies,* 29 (1968), 397-416, and *Revelation Theology: A History* (New York: Herder and Herder, 1969).

14 An account of this development, which is particularly interesting in that it represents a defense of progressivism by a man who has subsequently become a leading conservative, is Jean (now Cardinal) Daniélou, "A New Vision of Christian Origins: Judaeo-Christianity," *Cross Currents,* XVIII (1968), 163-73. See also R. Schnackenburg, *L'Eglise dans le Nouveau Testament,* French trans. by R. L. Oechslin, O.P. (Paris: Les Editions du Cerf, 1964), Deuxieme partie, pp. 65-71. Though Schnackenburg considers the Judaeo-Christians quite conservative, he absolves them of explicit heresy, e.g., in denying the divinity of Christ, as their successors, the Ebionites, did.

15 An excellent non-technical discussion of this point is contained in George MacRae, S.J., "Are the Gospels History" (to be published). For general background reading see Bruce Vawter, *The Four Gospels: An Introduction* (Garden City, N.Y.: Doubleday, 1967), Chap. I.

16 The functional nature of New Testament Christology was emphasized by Oscar Cullmann in *The Christology of the New Testament,* trans. S. Guthrie and C. Hall (Philadelphia: Westminster, 1959). An excellent recent discussion of this point is Yves Congar, O.P., "Christ in the Economy of Salvation and in Our Dogmatic Tracts," trans. A. Bourneuf, R.S.C.J., *Concilium,* Vol. 11 (*ed. cit.*), pp. 5-25.

17 A. Dulles in *Theological Studies* (footnote 13, above), 406.

18 In addition to the works of Grillmeier and Quasten already cited, the sources on which this outline of early doctrinal development depends are: Maurice Wiles, *The Making of Christian Doctrine: A Study in the Principles of Early Doctrinal Development* (Cambridge: Cambridge University Press, 1967); J. N. D. Kelly, *Early Christian Doctrines* (2nd ed.; New York: Harper & Row, 1960); J. Carmody, S.J. and T. Clarke, S.J., *Christ and His Mission* (*Sources of Christian Theology,* Vol. III) (West-

minster, Md.: Newman, 1966); and Bernard Lonergan, S.J., *De Deo Trino: Pars Analytica* (Rome: Gregorian University Press, 1961), pp. 13-113.

[19] This summary of his more detailed treatment is from Carmody and Clarke, *op. cit.*, p. xxxviii.

[20] These change-inducing factors are summarized in Wiles, *op. cit.*, Chap. II.

[21] The citation is from Wiles, *op. cit.*, pp. 32-33.

[22] This interpretation of the events at Nicea is based on Kelly, *op. cit.*, Chaps. VII and VIII.

[23] The key sentence of this text was cited earlier in the list of Christological statements given. The text is contained in many of the Patristic studies already cited, e.g., Carmody and Clarke, *op. cit.*, pp. 120-21.

[24] Grillmeier, *op. cit.*, p. 482.

[25] The pertinent texts may be found in Carmody and Clarke, *op. cit.*, pp. 245-61.

[26] Van Buren, *op. cit.*, Chap. II, gives a detailed evaluation of Chalcedon. Eventually he rejects this formulation of Christology as too mythological and misleading for the theological left and concentrates instead on a secular reinterpretation of the Gospel.

[27] L. Dewart, *op. cit.*, esp. Chap. IV.

[28] For a further discussion of the role such theorems played in Patristic Christology, see John McIntyre, *The Shape of Christology* (Philadelphia: Westminster, 1966), pp. 86-93.

[29] This is discussed in more detail in my "Linguistic Analysis..." (see footnote 1, above).

[30] St. Thomas Aquinas, *Summa Contra Gentiles*, Bk. 1, Chap. 30, #4.

[31] For further appraisals of the conceptual shortcomings of Chalcedon with respect to contemporary problems, see Wolfhart Pannenberg, *Jesus: God and Man*, trans. L. L. Wilkins and D. A. Priebe (Philadelphia: Westminster, 1968), pp. 283-307; McIntyre, *op. cit.*, Chap. IV; van Buren, *op. cit.*, Chap. II; and Karl Rahner, "Probleme der Christologie von heute" in his *Schriften Zur Theologie* (Einsiedlen: Benziger, 1959), Vol. I, pp. 169-222, esp. pp. 194-206. My own views on this problem were strongly conditioned by discussions with N. M. Wildiers.

[32] The relation between revelation and theology is explained in the *Summa Theologiae* (henceforth, *S. T.*), I, Q. 1.

[33] The divisions indicated here are those given by St. Thomas himself in the short introductions to new sections, e.g., *S. T.* I, Q. 2, introd.; Q. 44, introd.; I-II, introd. We have indicated such pivotal questions by putting the appropriate numbers in parentheses in the outline. A helpful general guide is M.-D. Chenu, O.P., *Towards Understanding St. Thomas*, trans. A. Landry, O.P. and D. Hughes, O.P. (Chicago: Regnery, 1963), pp. 310-18.

[34] For a survey of changing ideas on the nature of revelation see Dulles, *Revelation Theology* (see footnote 13, above) and the various articles in *Concilium*, Vol. 21, *Man as Man and Believer*, ed. E. Schillebeeckx (New York: Paulist Press, 1967).

[35] W. Pannenberg in *Theology as History*, eds. James M. Robinson and John B. Cobb, Jr. (New York: Harper and Row, 1967), p. 133.

[36] These ideas are developed in *S. T.*, II-II, Q. 1.

[37] This is discussed in Rudolf Schnackenburg, *The Truth Will Make You Free*, trans. R. Albrecht (New York: Herder and Herder, 1966), pp. 13-17. My ideas on scriptural teaching on truth rely heavily on Gabriel Moran, F.S.C., *Theology of Revelation* (New York: Herder and Herder, 1966).

[38] See *S. T.*, III, Q. 1, a. 3.

[39] For a fuller discussion of this, see W. A. Wallace, O.P., *The Role of Demonstration in Moral Theology: A Study of Methodology in St. Thomas Aquinas* (Washington, D. C.: The Thomist Press, 1962), pp. 36-47.

[40] *S. T.*, Q. 1, a. 7 for 'article of faith' and a. 8 for their being taught by Scripture.

[41] *S. T.*, I, Q. 2, a. 2, ad 1.

[42] *S. T.*, I, Q. 1, a. 9.

[43] That Thomas so interprets this text is clear, especially from *Summa Contra Gentiles*, Bk. 1, chap. 22, last paragraph. For a discussion of the importance this played in the thought of St. Thomas, see E. Gilson, *The Christian Philosophy of St. Thomas Aquinas*, trans. L. K. Shook, C.S.B. (5th ed.; New York: Random House) Part I, Chap. IV.

[44] *S. T.*, I, Q. 44, a. 1.

[45] *Ibid.*, a. 2, 3, 4.

[46] *S. T.*, I, Q. 68, a. 3, c.

[47] *S. T.*, I, Q. 66, a. 1, ad 1.

[48] *Ibid.*, ad 2 in contrarium. For further defenses of this idea of translating Moses' sensible doctrine into spiritual (i.e., philosophical) terms, see: *S. T.*, I, Q. 67, a. 4, c; Q. 69, a. 2, ad 3; Q. 70, a. 1, ad 3; Q. 74, a. 1, ad 2.

[49] *S. T.*, I, Q. 46, a. 2. St. Thomas does cite revelation as the exclusive basis for holding other truths, e.g., the doctrine of the Trinity in *S. T.* I, Q. 32, a. 1. Here, however, we are considering the truths that play the role of principles in explaining the constitution of creatures and their emanation from and return to God.

[50] These positions are summarized in Carmody and Clarke, *op. cit.*, pp. 191-95. The trichotomy was often expressed by asking whether Christ, as man, was someone, or something, or nothing.

[51] On this point, see Gottfried Geenan, O.P., "The Council of Chalcedon in the Theology of St. Thomas" in *From an Abundant Spring* (New York: P. J. Kenedy & Sons, 1952), pp. 172-217.

[52] See *S. T.*, III, Q. 2, a. 2 and Q. 17, a. 2. Here Thomas' reliance on Chalcedon is manifested in his "Sed Contra" citations, his normal way of bringing in an argument from authority. The idea that Jesus' human nature did not have its proper act of existence but received a communication of existence from the *Logos* had been a central feature in the *enhypostatic* theory of Leontius of Byzantium, an early post-Chalcedonian theologian. The critical edition of the *Summa* does not indicate any dependence of Thomas' thought on Leontius. However, he may have known of his views through the writings of St. John Damascene. In contemporary times this doctrine has been redeveloped in different ways by M. de la Taille and B. Lonergan and is still a viable position in Christology.

[53] The traditional explanation of this and other theological notes may be found in Ludwig Ott, *Fundamentals of Catholic Dogma* (2nd English ed.; St. Louis: B. Herder, 1955), pp. 8-10. The remainder of this handbook contains an almost exhaustive list of theological propositions proper to pre-Vatican II Catholic theology, each qualified by a theological note. For a more recent discussion of the significance to be attached to such notes see John J. Heaney, S.J., "Catholic Hermeneutics, the Magisterium, and Infallibility," *Continuum,* VII (1969), 106-19.

[54] The basic article here is Rudolf Bultmann, "New Testament and Mythology," in Hans Werner Bartsch (ed.), *Kerygma and Myth: A Theological Debate,* trans. R. H. Fuller (London: S.P.C.K., 1953).

[55] Bultmann, *op. cit.,* p. 10.

[56] Some criticisms which I found helpful were: Henri Bouillard, *The Logic of Faith,* trans. M. H. Gill & Sons, Ltd. (New York: Sheed and Ward, 1967), Chap. VI; van Buren, *op. cit.,* Chap. III, who summarizes the outstanding criticisms; and the criticisms in the Bartsch volume. A good brief summary of Bultmann and the post-Bultmannian developments may be found in John S. Kselman, S.S., "Modern New Testament Criticism," in *The Jerome Bible Commentary* (Englewood Cliffs, N. J.: Prentice-Hall, 1968), Vol. II, pp. 7-20.

[57] This quotation is taken from Karl Barth, *Church Dogmatics: A Selection,* trans. and ed., G. W. Bromiley (New York: Harper Torchbook, 1961), p. 72.

[58] Donald Evans, *Religious Language and Divine Transcendence* (to be published), Chap. III. I wish to thank Professor Evans for allowing me to read a prepublication copy of this work.

[59] *S. T.,* III, Q. 2, a. 2, c.

[60] This quotation is taken from Carmody and Clarke, *op. cit.,* p. 237.

[61] Pannenberg, *Jesus, God and Man, ed. cit.,* Chaps. VIII and IX. A detailed discussion of his views may be found in James M. Robinson and John B. Cobb, Jr. (eds.), *Theology of History, ed. cit.,* which contains an article by Pannenberg summarizing his revelational view of the Incarnation, critical discussions of this position by different theologians, and a reply by Pannenberg.

[62] P. van Buren, *op. cit.,* Part II.

[63] A summary of different Christian Christological models may be found in McIntyre, *op. cit.*

[64] W. R. Matthews, *The Problem of Christ in the Twentieth Century: An Essay on the Incarnation* (London: Oxford University Press, 1950), Chaps. III and IV.

[65] Dorothee Sölle, *Christ the Representative: An Essay in Theology after the "Death of God,"* trans. D. Lewis (Philadelphia: Fortress Press, 1967), Part Three.

[66] This criticism was contained in my article, "The Truth of Belief," *America,* 116 (April 15, 1967), 553-56. 1 found his recent work, *The Foundations of Belief* (New York: Herder & Herder, 1969), more acceptable. However, Christology is not one of the basic concerns of this book.

[67] Ansgar Hulsbosch, "Jezus Christus, gekend als mens, beleden als Zoon Gods," *Tijdschrift voor Theologie* 6 (1966), 250-73. Rejoinders by E. Schillebeeckx and P. Schoonenberg are in the same issue. I wish to

thank M. Wildiers for summarizing these articles for me. An English extension of this discussion may be found in Robert North, S.J. "Soul-Body Unity and God-Man Unity," *Theological Studies,* 30 (1969), 27-60; and "Recent Christology and Theological Method," *Continuum,* VII (1969), 63-77.

[68] The reasons supporting this judgment may be found in my "Analysis and the Philosophy of Science," *International Philosophical Quarterly,* VII (1967), 213-50.

INDEX